ORDER FORM

England R

Post to:
INNOVATIONS (Mail Order
Euroway Business Park
Swindon SN5 8SN Phone: 07

VICE. As a se
ke our customer
es whose produ
u do not wish t
copy of your ad
s Park, Swindon
prices valid until 30th June 1994. After this da
our Customer Service Department for advic
order. Prices were correct at time of going
reserve the right to amend prices in the event
the rate of VAT.

ORDERED BY

(Mr/Mrs/Miss/Ms) First Name

Surname

Address

Postcode

Daytime Tel. No.
(in case of enquiries)

DELIVER TO

Fill in only if different from "ORDERED BY"

Name

Address

Postcode

ITEMS ORDERED

(BLOCK CAPITALS PLEASE)

Page No	Item Code	Size	Colour	Description	Personalisation (BLOCK CAPITALS)	Item Price £	Qty
	HA11052	My order totals £50 or more and I claim my Auto Light for £1.00				1.00	1
						Postage and Packing	
						Handling Charge (see our Policy, opposite) FREE on orders over £20 Please delete as applicable	
						HA18878 My Donation to the British Heart Foundation	

BLOCK CAPITALS PLEASE

METHOD OF PAYMENT

1 CREDIT CARD 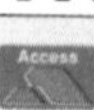   

Please debit my Access/Visa/American Express/Diners Club card *please circle choice

2 BY CHEQUE OR POSTAL ORDER

I enclose cheque/postal order for:

The items in this book are not available for sale.
The 'order form' is for illustrative purposes only and the address and telephone numbers are no longer valid.

First published in Great Britain in 2004

Bloomsbury Publishing Plc,
38 Soho Square, London W1D 3HB

A CIP catalogue record for this book is available from the British Library

ISBN 07475-7346-8

10 9 8 7 6 5 4 3 2 1

All papers used by Bloomsbury Publishing are natural, recyclable products made from wood grown in well-managed forests. The manufacturing processes conform to the environmental regulations of the country of origin.

Printed In Singapore by Tien Wah Press

Contents

Gadgets & Technology 1

Garden & DIY 13

Household 29

Wellbeing 55

Leisure 83

Cars & Travel 91

Pets 97

THE INNOVATIONS REPORT

VOLUME XV NUMBER ONE

AUTUMN/WINTER 1991

THE WORLD INNOVATION

A BUYERS GUIDE

Add professional sound effects to your videos

Bring extra humour and interest to your home video productions with the superb Boing Box Sound Effects Mixer. Boing Box contains 59 digitalised natural sound effects, plus electronic tunes and arcade sounds you can call up at the touch of a button. Add a barking dog, a creaking door, applause, laughter, breaking glass etc. – or play around with the Special Effects Facility to modify the built-in sounds, giving you literally thousands of different sound effects to choose from. Boing Box is also a sophisticated three-channel audio mixer, permitting you to add narration or music from tape, CD, record or another VCR. Simple to use, Boing Box comes with full instructions, 240v mains adaptor and connecting leads.

Boing Box £249.95 OJ406

Answer your phone with 16 different voices

Be whoever you want to be with this clever voice changing telephone. You simply choose one of the 16 different programmable voices at the touch of a button, and change your male voice into a female's, your adult voice into a child's and vice versa. Making or receiving phone calls has never been such fun. Also includes last number redial, tone/pulse switching, and on/off ringer. AC adaptor and modular phone jack supplied.

Voice Changer Phone £49.95 FE745B

Keeps you on budget and on time

Whether you travel for business or pleasure, the affordable Travelator will be your constant companion. This multi-functional tool comprises a dual-time clock/calendar, dual bi-level alarm (with snooze) to get you up and keep you on your daily schedule, calculator and interactive currency converter. But where Travelator becomes truly invaluable is its easy-to-use Fund Management System. You can quickly tap in your daily expenditure as it happens, categorised by expense type. If travelling on a budget, you can enter daily/weekly/overall allowances to prevent overspending – and finally, you can call up 8 handy financial reports of spending to date. Measures 11 x 6.2 x 1cm (4" x 2⅜" x ⅜"). Batteries included.
Travelator £24.95 KA29936

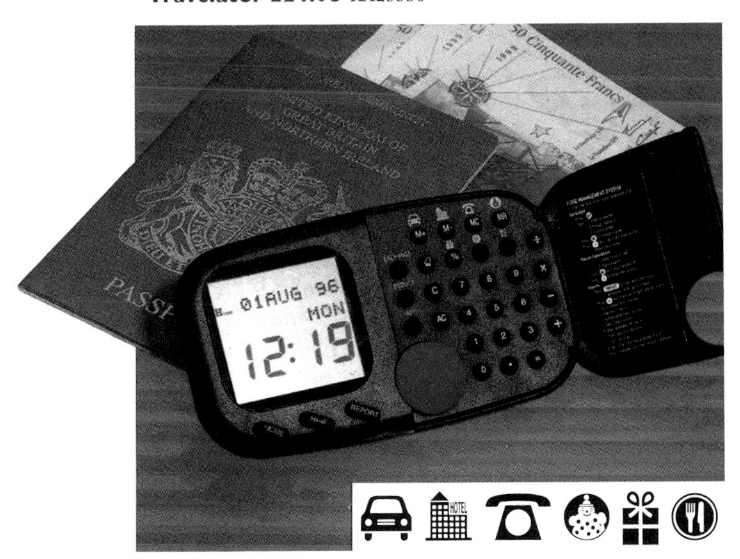

The Electro-Luminescent Clock

You may already have admired wristwatches with innovative luminescent dials, but you probably haven't seen a clock with this remarkable new technology. When you press the top button on the Electro-Luminescent Alarm Clock, the entire face is backlit with a subtle warm blue glow. The effect is absolutely stunning, so much so it's easy to overlook the other qualities of the clock. It has a classic analogue face set within a beautifully-designed case, plus 3-stage crescendo alarm that wakes you gently yet insistently. Powered by single AA battery (not supplied). 5" x 4" x 2".

Luminescent Alarm Clock
£19.95 NA25693

Any pen can write. This one talks, too ...

Why do the most brilliant ideas always seem to occur when you're away from your desk? Now, thanks to the unique Pencorder, you can capture those pearls of wisdom wherever you are - in the car, in the lift, walking down the street! The Pencorder is the world's first writing instrument with a built-in digital recorder. Using advanced customised semi-conductor chips, it holds up to 40 seconds of speech - and plays it back with telephone clarity via a miniature loudspeaker that produces very high quality sound. The pen's casing is made from aerospace-grade matte-finish titanium that offers light weight (only 2oz overall), armour-tough protection and resistance to corrosion. Comfortable writing action is ensured by a soft Griptex nose cone, while inside there's a premium-quality tungsten-carbide ballpoint (one refill also provided). Pencorder is powered by 4 x LR-44 alkaline cells (supplied), and measures 5½" x ⅝".

Pencorder £99.95 FH766D

"Quick, before I forget ... it's E = MC2!"

Levitating pen

Place Pen-Ultimate on its stand and it 'floats' without any visible means of support. There is, of course, a rational scientific explanation – namely, the forces of magnetism. Give it a gentle spin and it clearly demonstrates the inter-actional relationship between magnetism, gravity, friction, the chaos theory and rotational inertia (it also makes a delightful pattern).

Pen-Ultimate
£7.99 IA18263

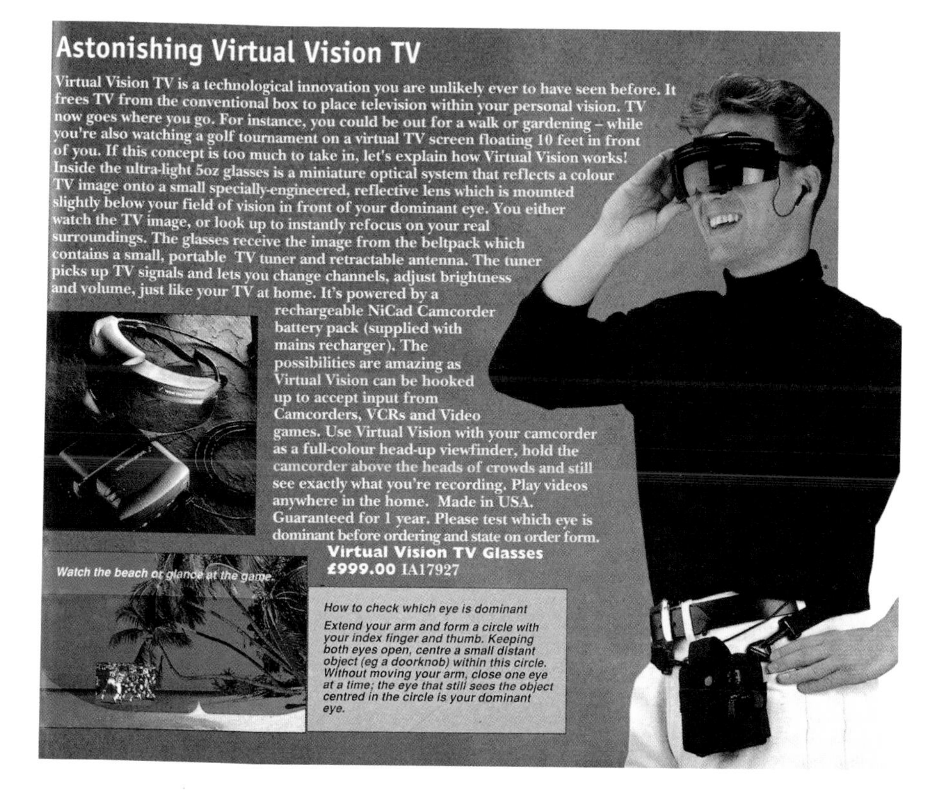
Astonishing Virtual Vision TV
Virtual Vision TV is a technological innovation you are unlikely ever to have seen before. It frees TV from the conventional box to place television within your personal vision. TV now goes where you go. For instance, you could be out for a walk or gardening – while you're also watching a golf tournament on a virtual TV screen floating 10 feet in front of you. If this concept is too much to take in, let's explain how Virtual Vision works! Inside the ultra-light 5oz glasses is a miniature optical system that reflects a colour TV image onto a small specially-engineered, reflective lens which is mounted slightly below your field of vision in front of your dominant eye. You either watch the TV image, or look up to instantly refocus on your real surroundings. The glasses receive the image from the beltpack which contains a small, portable TV tuner and retractable antenna. The tuner picks up TV signals and lets you change channels, adjust brightness and volume, just like your TV at home. It's powered by a rechargeable NiCad Camcorder battery pack (supplied with mains recharger). The possibilities are amazing as Virtual Vision can be hooked up to accept input from Camcorders, VCRs and Video games. Use Virtual Vision with your camcorder as a full-colour head-up viewfinder, hold the camcorder above the heads of crowds and still see exactly what you're recording. Play videos anywhere in the home. Made in USA. Guaranteed for 1 year. Please test which eye is dominant before ordering and state on order form.
Virtual Vision TV Glasses
£999.00 IA17927
Watch the beach or glance at the game.
How to check which eye is dominant
Extend your arm and form a circle with your index finger and thumb. Keeping both eyes open, centre a small distant object (eg a doorknob) within this circle. Without moving your arm, close one eye at a time; the eye that still sees the object centred in the circle is your dominant eye.

The radio that thinks it's a PC

Cleverly designed to look like a miniature computer this FM/AM (VHF/MW) radio boasts outstanding clear crisp sound that belies its size. The monitor conceals a directional speaker and it comes complete with a telescopic FM aerial and personal headphone jackpoint. 11.7cm (4½") high. AC/DC – uses 3 AA batteries or run it off the mains with an adaptor (neither supplied).

PC Radio £14.95 52842

Radio-controlled accuracy now under £25

When radio-controlled timekeeping technology was introduced not so long ago, you expected to pay £100 or more to find it in a wristwatch. Today, the cost of the same technology has come down to an amazing £24.95. It's no idle claim when we say this is the world's most accurate watch. The case contains a miniature antenna that receives a radio time signal based on the Caesium Atomic Clock – accurate to within a second in a million years! The watch automatically adjusts itself to British Summer and Winter Time; and if travelling outside the 900-mile signal range or to another time zone, can be manually adjusted in one-hour increments. LCD display shows hours, minutes, seconds, day and date. Battery included.

Radio-Controlled Watch £24.95 NA25692

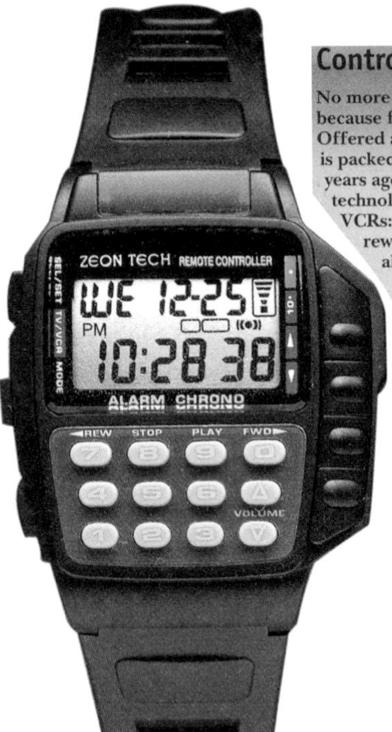

Control TV and video – from your watch

No more frantic searching for the remote control handset - because from now on, you could be wearing it on your wrist! Offered at a breakthrough £29.95, this Remote Control Watch is packed with miniaturised hi-tech features that only a few years ago would have been undreamt of. Its powerful infrared technology controls all basic functions of most TVs and VCRs: power on/off, volume, channel selection, video play, rewind, fast forward and stop. And if this isn't enough, it also boasts a full set of timekeeping functions too: the 12 digit LCD display shows hours, minutes, seconds, month, date and day, with daily/hourly alarms plus stopwatch facilities including elapsed/split times and 2 finish times. The TV Remote Control Watch can be programmed to work most makes – see chart below for reference. Battery supplied.

TV Remote Control Watch £29.95
NA25697

THE TV REMOTE CONTROL WATCH CAN BE PROGRAMMED TO OPERATE THESE BRANDS OF TVs & VCRs

TELEVISIONS	VIDEO CASSETTE RECORDERS
HITACHI	GOLDSTAR
TOSHIBA	HITACHI
SANYO	MITSUBISHI
SONY	PANASONIC
MITSUBISHI	PHILIPS
PANASONIC	SAMSUNG
SHARP	SANYO
PHILIPS/SAMSUNG/GOLDSTAR	SHARP
ELBE	TOSHIBA
NEC	

Your portable personal astrologer

Unlike newspaper horoscopes, this unique electronic astrological guide provides you with instant access to a daily horoscope based on your birth date, not just your astrological sign. Simply key in your birthday details and today's date, then scroll through your personal 'reading' on the 2-line LCD screen. You can also call up personality profiles to find out what horoscopes reveal about you, or anyone else. Find out whether you are compatible with lovers or friends by keying in both birth dates. Discover the birthdays of over 700 famous people from Marilyn Monroe to Elvis Presley! Other features include user-list to store up to 10 names and birthdays *built-in astrology tutorial *on-screen help *selectable type sizes *demonstration mode. Comes with battery and carry case. 4" x 2½" x ¼".
Pocket Astrologer £39.95 NA25867

was £79.99
now £69.9
save £10
(see page 23 for full detail
1/2 pric
Sony splas
proof radi
ONLY £19.
with orders ove
see page 41 for
v.innovations.co.uk

Bag an award-winning idea

There's nothing more frustrating than trying to fill a bag while holding it open at the same time. Now Flexi-Ring, winner of the 1990 Design Council Award, will hold and support any size paper or plastic bag so you can fill it with ease. This tough, self-locking expandable ring is ideal for use with garden sacks, DIY rubbish bags etc. It comes with a clip-on, height-adjustable stand, that can be wall-mounted or positioned in soft ground near where you're working. It's like having an extra pair of hands!

Flexi-Ring Bag Holder £5.95
FG400A

Rest easy when Securi-Gnome is on guard duty

The British-made Securi-Gnome may look like an innocent garden ornament - but in fact, he's an effective sentry for your home. The sturdy plastic Securi-Gnome contains a cunningly disguised PIR body heat sensor and he can be placed anywhere up to 20ft from the house. Unwanted intruders will be bathed in bright halogen floodlight the moment they come into range. Of course, your welcome visitors will be provided with a convenient courtesy light as they near your door. Standing 18" high, Securi-Gnome is powered using a safe low 12 volt supply with 10m of cable. He comes with a 500 watt open halogen lamp for mounting on an existing dual socket box. He can be pegged down into the earth or screwed onto a concrete base. Full instructions are provided for installation by electrician or competent DIYer. Available in brown terracotta (TC) or grey stone colours (GS).

Securi-Gnome System (TC)
£79.95 FE951
Securi-Gnome System (GS)
£79.95 FE960

A giant helping hand for gardeners

If you've ever wished you had bigger hands when faced with a mountain of leaves or grass cuttings to clear up, then Giant Hands answer your prayer! They increase your hand size by about three times, making rubbish clearance faster and more effective. The 14" concave scoops enable you to pick up vast amounts of garden debris in each 'handful', and because they're made of durable plastic, you're safely protected from thorns and cuts. In an unmissable colour you can't lose amongst the grass clippings!
Giant Hands £7.95 FG561A

Doggy Bootscraper

A fun item that is both attractive and practical. Shaped like a Sausage Dog or Dachshund, this quality cast iron bootscaper also acts as a doorstop. Do away with muddy boots or shoes through your hall and put a smile on the faces of your guests.

Dog Bootscraper
£14.95 OG832

Scare away unwanted garden guests

Believe it or not, these lifelike 16½" plastic-moulded models can help to discourage birds, squirrels and other rodents from eating fruit, vegetables or seedlings in your garden – the cat is also useful for helping to protect fish ponds from predators. Hand-painted with large realistic eyes, they come from the USA where they sell by the thousand (the owl is the same one used to keep pigeons off many public buildings). A capped hole in the base lets you mount the models on a pole, or fill with sand for standing securely anywhere in the garden.

Cat £16.95 OG815
Owl £16.95 OG816

Scare Cat garden protector

If you're tired of neighbours' cats messing up your garden, or raids by birds and squirrels, here's a beautifully simple way to help solve the problem for just £4.95. Scare Cat is a realistic 14½" x 7" feline shape with glowing glass eyes on a painted black metal body. Fully weatherproof, she stays out all year, helping to guard against unwanted visitors.

Scare Cat £4.95 NC17423

Pocket Chain Saw cuts higher, lower – and faster ▶

The teeth of this stowaway chain saw cut on three sides simultaneously and in both directions – that's far more efficient than any normal saw. But where this design really scores over hand saws is its sheer versatility. You can get it under tree roots for easy cutting below ground level – or, using the approx. 5m (16¼ft) polypropylene extension cord, you can throw it over high branches for pruning without a ladder. Lightweight and portable in its waterproof canvas pouch, the approx. 80cm (31½") saw has 140 self-sharpening heat-strengthened steel teeth that cut through wood, brick, plastic piping and many other materials. Ideal for the gardener, DIYer and camper. We recommend that the user wears head, hand and face protection when using the saw. The user should also stand well clear of falling material when cutting elevated branches.

Pocket Chain Saw £35.00 DA23567

Make your own cast-iron house name plaque

Here's a simple, fast and fun way to create an original name or number plaque that will add individual character to your home. The solid cast-iron plaques come in a variety of classic shapes and sizes: a large 'bridge' design 44.4 x 17.7cm (17½" x 7"), an elegant oval 32 x 17cm (12½" x 6¾") or, if you prefer only a numberplate, a small 'bridge' 16.6 x 14cm (6⅞" x 5⅞"). Each kit contains everything required to design and make your one-off plaque: a sheet of transfers including bird, animal and flower designs, a wide selection of precision moulded plastic letters and numbers; special adhesive to apply your chosen letters or numbers; glossy colour paints and varnish, plus paint brushes, together with the necessary wall fixings and simple illustrated step-by-step instructions.

Large Bridge House Name Kit
£49.95 PA28875
Oval House Name Kit
£39.95 PA28874
House Number Kit £27.95 PA28873

Protect flowers from the trailing hose

Here's the quickest solution to an age-old problem – how to prevent your garden hose from dragging across flowerbeds and shrubs, potentially flattening the lot! These hose guides are the answer. Using a hammer or mallet, simply drive them into the ground at the edge of beds and borders to create a controlled 'path' for the hose to follow as you work up the garden. The broad tops keep the hose at ground level, while the rotating centre sleeves allow the hose to be pulled out easily. 30.5cm (12") long; made from UV stabilised plastic.
Hose Guide (single) £6.95 PA29206
(set of three) £18.00 PA29207

A unique plant labelling system

These clever new plant markers not only allow you to label each flower, shrub or tree in your garden but also to keep a record of their growing instructions and 'history', plus the chance to colour-code care requirements for instant visual reference. First unscrew the cap and write the plant's name and details on the label with a ballpoint (to re-use, wipe off with nail polish remover). Before reclosing the weather-resistant barrel you can also include the rolled-up seed packet or further handwritten notes for future reference. Finally, each marker also has an ingenious colour-coding window. Using the choice of six colours, you can see at a glance whether a plant is frost-prone, needs to be pruned after flowering, is prone to slug damage etc.
Gardian Plant Markers (5)
£4.95 PA30785
Gardian Plant Markers (10)
£9.90 PA30786

Make your own ornamental stepping stones

This original DIY idea certainly gives the term 'leaf mould' a new meaning! Take your pick from the 4 attractive natural designs, each modelled on a different species of deciduous leaf – and with minimal effort and simple materials, cast your own decorative paving slabs at a fraction of the cost of bought ones. The kit comprises four flexible plastic moulds depicting maple, beech, oak and sycamore leaves, each 30 x 3.5cm (approx 11⅘" x 1⅖"). To make a slab, fill the mould with readymix cement (requires just under 9lb per slab) and turn out the completed stone when fully set. If desired, you can include colour additives in the cement or set a ring of bent wire into the reverse to create a charming outdoor wallhanging.

Stepping Stone Moulds (4) £10.95 KA33571

Ever wished for a garden fountain?

This charming Wishing Well instantly adds the restful sound of trickling water to your garden or conservatory. Powered by a low voltage mains supply, it's self-contained and ready to run - just fill with water, plug in and switch on. Crafted from weather-resistant treated softwood (with strong metal hoops around the half-barrel base), it contains a waterproof liner and a concealed self-circulating pump. Whether kept indoors or out, it requires minimal maintenance and cleaning, and costs very little to operate. 76 cm high, 48 cm diameter. (indoor or covered patio use).

Free delivery with this product.

Wishing Well Fountain **£99.99** MV0776

4 easy payments of £25.00

Insulated by nature

This clever British-designed Milk Bottle Planter is not only practical but well disguised. You fill the outer rim with soil or compost and plant it with pretty flowers or small shrubs. The soil provides superb natural insulation for the lidded central compartment which holds four milk bottles, fully protected against sub-zero winter temperatures, summer heat and the attacks of birds. Made from weatherproof terracotta-colour moulded plastic. Approx 14⅝" diameter.

Milk Bottle Planter £11.99 WA20775

Terracotta outdoor information centre

Now you can keep an eye on the time and the temperature while you're outside, enjoying the garden. This stylish matching clock and thermometer are fully weatherproofed, allowing them to be permanently mounted to any wall, tree or fence post. Both have hand-sculpted and polished terracotta faces, measure 12½" in diameter, allowing them to be easily read from a distance. Clock requires 1 x AA battery (not supplied).

Terracotta Clock £24.99 WB13813
Terracotta Thermometer £24.99 WB13814

At last, the 100% robotic lawnmower

new

The time has come to trade in your old mower for a hammock! The RL500 Robomower, from Friendly Robotics, is a fully robotic domestic lawnmower, capable of mowing an area the size of a tennis court in just over 2 hours ... all on its own. Just lay the guide wire approximately 45cm inside the outer edges of your lawn, then connect it to a small perimeter switch. The wire will soon be covered in grass so you won't know it's there. The RL500 is loaded with innovative sensors to keep it within the active perimeter, plus tactile bumper sensors which change direction if it encounters solid obstacles. And because it mows in a triangular pattern from many different directions, it can cut any lawn regardless of shape, slopes (up to 15°), paths etc. It also mulches as it mows, so there's no need to bag up the cut grass! Other features include: 53cm overall cut with 3 mulching blades

4 easy payments of £187.25

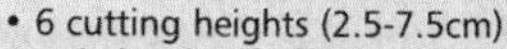

- 6 cutting heights (2.5-7.5cm)
- switches itself off when finished
- override facility permits use as a manual mower • 32 x 66 x 90cm, weighs 78lbs
- kit includes rechargeable battery pack, charger, wire, stakes, manual controller, user manual, instructional video.

Free delivery with this product.

RL500 Robomower **£749.00** MG6771

exclusive

H E • R E P O R T
Spring 1993
ISAAC NEWTON
(1643-1727)
Discovered the laws of mechanics and of gravity, as well as the foundations of mathematical calculus.
TRIMEASY
A simple mechanical action of 2 chisel tip blades transformed by battery power into a superb decorating tool. See page 52.
THE TELL TAIL GOLF BALL
The clever practice ball that scales down flight to around one tenth. See page 4.
HIT THE BALL OVER THE TAIL
TURN ON THE HUMAN CALCULATOR IN YOU!
TURN ON THE
THE HUMAN CALCULATOR
SCOTT FLANSBURG
HUMAN CALCULATOR
4
3
2
THE HUMAN CALCULATOR

Sleeve Holders are back!

Sleeve Holders have come right back into fashion - and they're still the most practical way to keep your sleeves up! These attractive gold and silver coloured metallic Sleeve Holders look great with any shirt, blouse or jacket, and are especially useful with today's baggy sweaters. Choose from the Single Strand wavy tubular design - two pairs, one in each colour, for only £7.95. Or a single pair of the Triple Strand tube design in either colour for only £6.95 a pair. All come in one size and stretch to fit.

Single Strand Sleeve Holders (Two pairs) £7.95 FR237
Triple Strand Sleeve Holders (Gold Colour Pair) £6.95 FR238
Triple Strand Sleeve Holders (Silver Colour Pair) £6.95 FR239

Over-the-door ironing organiser

This clever Ironing Station lets you save space by hanging both your ironing board and iron neatly out of the way on the back of a door or on the wall. Sturdily made from metal with a heavy-duty plastic coating for years of use, the Ironing Station measures 18⅜" x 7½" x 3⅝", holds most irons and boards and fits any standard cupboard or spare room door. Comes complete with all fixtures and fittings.

Ironing Station
£9.95 FD397

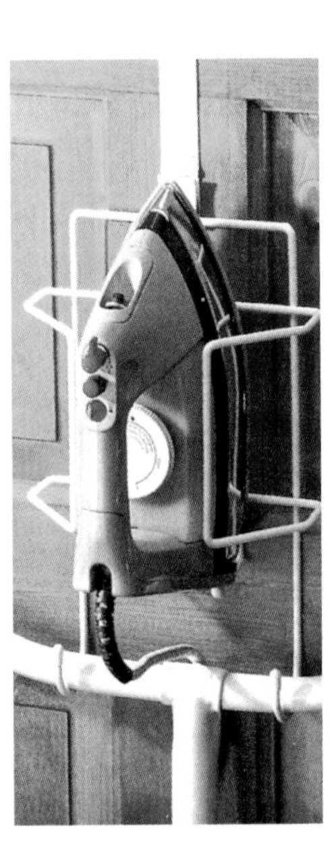

Fast Track, the ultimate tie & belt organiser

If you're still storing your tie collection over a clothes hanger in the wardrobe, Fast Track is a great way to get them properly organised in minimal space. It not only neatly stores up to 72 ties or belts (in any combination) but also features a motorised selection system that makes it much easier to make your choice for the day. At the push of a button, the entire track rotates (in either direction) to present the ties or belts for your consideration. Moreover, an integral light lets you search in the dark so you need not disturb your partner if making an early start. Fast Track measures just 5" wide and mounts directly onto your existing wardrobe rail. Uses 2 x D batteries (not supplied).

Fast Track £29.95 NA25601

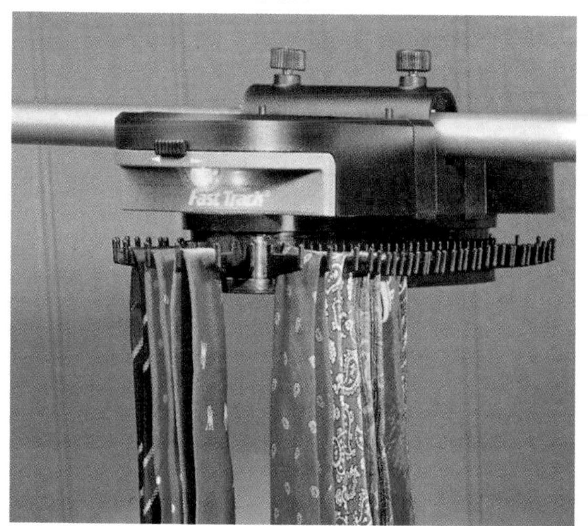

The tie that ZIPS up!

If you hate fiddling about every morning trying to tie the perfect knot - or if your hands simply aren't as nimble as they used to be - then discover the innovative Zipper Tie. Using the clever zip mechanism, you just tighten up the tie to your neck size; you never need to re-do the neat knot. Made from 100% polyester, Zipper Ties are available in two classic designs.

Zipper Tie (Stripe) £6.95
FS078A

Zipper Tie (Polka Dot) £6.95
FS079A

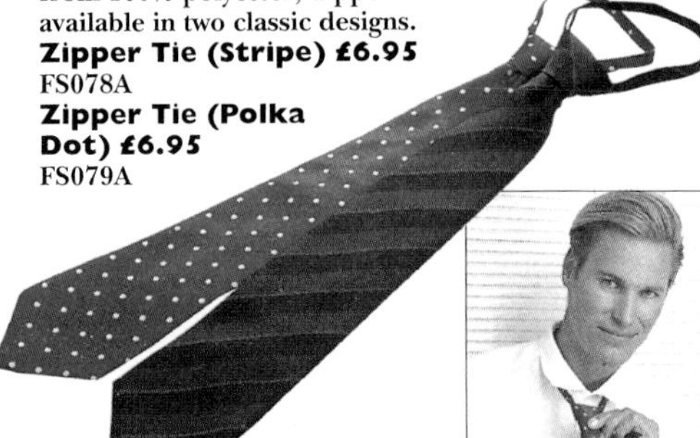

Your Family Name History

These beautiful framed certificates give you and your family a unique insight into the origin and meaning of your surname. You could find out the earliest recorded usage of the name, its geographical origins, famous bearers of the names, interesting historical anecdotes – even a coat of arms, when relevant. Printed on high-quality parchment-effect paper in a decorative typeface, each certificate is signed and authenticated by the researcher. Perspex-fronted gilt frame measures 14⅝" x 11½" (certificate also available unframed at 14" x 11"). Please state surname required in personalisation column on order form. Most British, European and African surnames available.

Certificate (framed) £29.95 FL671
Certificate (unframed) £11.95 FL670

1	8	15	22
2	9	16	23
3	10	17	24
4	11	18	25
5	12	19	26
6	13	20	27
7	14	21	28

Address labels with a difference!

Self-adhesive name and address labels are such a useful idea. But with a choice of 36 different designs, these new picture labels add the extra touch of personalisation! Whether you're an animal-lover, sports fan, musician, simply select your favourite design to appear beside the pre-printed details. You can personalise with your name, address and phone number (or any other wording), up to 18 letters and spaces on each of six lines. When ordering, please state the design code required in the 'Size' column and your required text in 'Personalisation' column of the Order Form. The 19 x 40mm labels come in packs of 500 and are available with either white or gold backgrounds.

500 Picture Address Labels
(white) £5.95 OH901
(gold) £5.95 OH903

Watch TV from the best seat in the house!

Why is it that so many people prefer to sit on the floor in front of the telly? Whatever the reason, here's the best way to do it! Our new lightweight TV Chair looks great, folds almost completely flat when not in use - and is so comfortable you'll never want to sit straight onto the floor again. The frame is made of sturdy black-enamelled tubing, covered with heavy-duty 10oz cotton canvas with a padded seat section. It's especially good for playing TV games, and also makes a space-saving occasional chair for indoor or outdoor use. Measures 17" x 25" x 24".

TV Chair £24.95 FC458

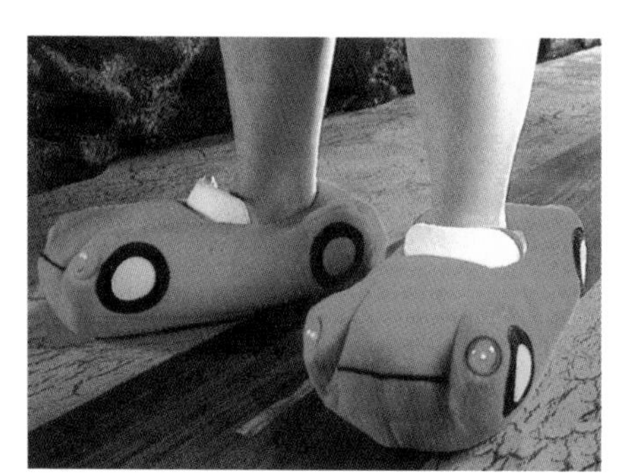

Step into full-beam slippers!

Car-shaped slippers with built-in headlights; simply a bit of innovative fun or a genuine safety idea? The truth is, they're actually both! Made of plush red 80% dacron/20% cotton, with 100% cotton linings and non-slip PVC outsoles, they are warm and comfortable - and when you step into them, those powerful headlights are automatically switched on, safely lighting your way in the dark. Headlight Slippers are currently available in three sizes (3-4, 5-6, 7-8). Please state size required in 'Size' column on Order Form. Uses 4 x AA batteries (not supplied)

Headlight Slippers £19.95 FA271

Catch spiders the easy way

This brilliant Spider Catcher lets you scoop up spiders and other unwanted insects and deposit them safely back outside without any harm to the insect, you or your nerves! The scoop is operated by a finger trigger, and a 36" long handle not only helps you reach insects in difficult places – high up on the ceiling or wall, for instance – but also lets you do it at arm's length! Made from durable plastic, we think it's a real winner!

Spider Catcher £7.95 FE497D

Create expert pelmets and drapes in minutes

Until now, creating sophisticated drapes and pelmets has needed professional expertise. But like all brilliant ideas, Window Wiz makes it so easy and fast! It comprises a rigid plastic frame that screws into place over the window. You simply pull the material through the holes, fluff it out and drape the surplus fabric at the sides. Each frame is 30" long and can be cut to size – for wider windows use two or more. Also available is an instructional video, packed with different styles and great ideas.

Window Wiz (3) £9.99 IA17145

Window Wiz (3) plus Video £14.99 IA18248

1. Two simple screw fittings and Window Wiz is in place

2. Thread the fabric through the loops to form 'pockets'

3. Fluff out the pockets and arrange drapes at side

The bin that's almost too good for rubbish!

£89.99 for a waste bin? Sounds a lot, but then this is far from an ordinary bin. For a start, it's hand-made entirely from solid mahogany, grown in sustained Indonesian forests. Based on a traditional colonial design, it features intricate hand-cut fretwork and is quite superbly finished. Heavy and sturdy, this bin should last for many years – a delightful addition to your home or office. Measures 13" x 11" x 8".

Mahogany Waste Bin
£89.99 IA14218

A lap tray in real wood

Our new 16" x 12" lap tray is beautifully made with a natural-finish real wood top, specially treated to resist knocks, scratches, heat or water stains. A lipped edge prevents cups, plates or spilt liquids sliding off, while the fabric-covered base is filled with tiny polystyrene beads that mould comfortably to your lap, forming a safe, stable surface. Ideal for TV dinners, breakfast in bed, jigsaws, hobbies, letter writing, sketching etc.

Tray-Knee
£14.99
WA12128

The ribetting Frog Phone

Froggy sits on his rock waiting for the call. And when it comes, he informs you with an hilarious electronic 'Ribet! Ribet!'. It makes an entertaining change from the normal ring or buzz and we think you'll agree he certainly looks a lot more interesting than any ordinary telephone! Under the rock you'll find a modern one-piece telephone with digital keypad, last number redial and tone/pulse switching. Measures 7¼"L x 5"H x 4½"W.

Frog Phone £44.99
IA16988

PROHIBITED from direct or indirect connection to public telecommunication systems. Action may be taken against anyone so connecting this apparatus.

PARP PARP! It's for you ...

If you're a motorcycle freak, here's the only phone for you! The Kawasaki Phone is a superb 11" x 6½" x 2½" scale model of the Ninja series racing superbike, faithfully reproducing its sleek fairing and gleaming chromed fittings, and mounted on an impressive plinth. However, nestling under the tank and seat there lies an equally modern two-piece telephone, with push-button dialling, last number redial and pulse/tone switching. The best touch of all? Incoming calls are announced with a realistic horn noise and flashing of headlights!
Kawasaki Phone £54.99 IA12424

Create your own ice sculptures

If you've ever wondered how caterers create those beautiful ice sculptures, here's the secret. Most are not actually 'sculpted' but are made in moulds exactly like these! It's incredibly easy to do – you simply fill the latex mould with water (or chocolate for a real indulgence!) and place it in the freezer upside down in its cradle. When fully frozen, the mould peels off to reveal an exquisitely detailed sculpture that will take centre-stage on any dining table. Choose from the Lobster design (12" x 5" x 6") or the elegant Swan (12" x 5" x 6").

Ice Sculpture Lobster £16.99 WA21418
Ice Sculpture Swan £16.99 WA20772

Keep bread warm at the table

It may look like an ordinary woven cane bread basket with a pretty paisley cotton cover – but that's only half the story. Because this innovative Bread Warmer also contains a thermostatically-controlled heating element designed to keep the contents at around 70°c, the perfect temperature for hot food. It can be used for a vast variety of breads: pitta, hot rolls, toast, poppadoms, naan bread, croissants, garlic bread – even baked potatoes! It's also great for 'late arrivals' and will keep a plate warm, with food covered in foil ... without drying out the contents. Basket measures approx 12" diameter; 100% cotton cover detaches for machine washing. Mains-powered, 240V AC.

Bread Warmer Basket
£29.99 WA20560

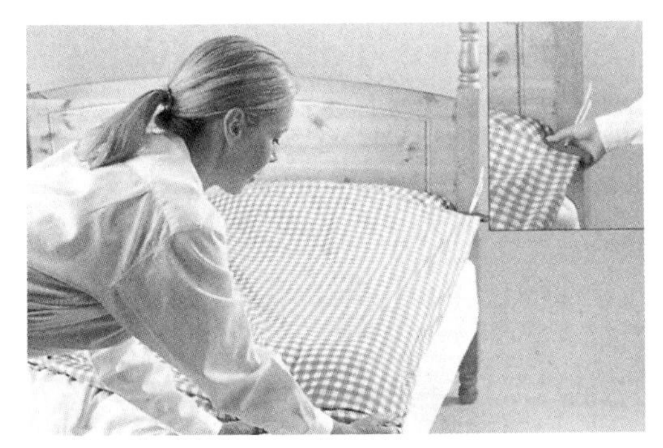

Changing duvet covers made easy!

Changing a duvet cover is a time-consuming hassle for two people and a nightmare if a solo effort! But now with this ingeniously simple British invention, one person can do the whole job in seconds. Tuck the top two corners of the duvet into the corresponding corners of the cover and secure each in place with a Bed's Maid clip. Then loop the cord over the headboard (or round the mattress) and simply pull the rest of the cover down over the duvet – it's like having an extra pair of hands!

Bed's Maid £6.95 NA25293

Unfold the 'instant' ironing board
If the whole business of getting your ironing board out (and clearing a space to set it up) has become a hassle, you'll love this ingenious time- and space-saving invention. Iron Mate is a completely new board design which folds up into a slim (3" deep) wall-mounted unit when not required. It's up and ready for use in seconds with just three simple actions, and packs away again just as quickly. Iron Mate has a robust galvanised steel frame and features a steam-resistant board base with cotton canvas cover – and because it's permanently fixed to the wall and has no 'legs', it is also extremely stable and cannot be knocked over by children or pets. Closed size approx 24" x 13¾" x 3".
Iron Mate £49.99 WAI9701

GOJO insulated mug for people on the move

How often do you leave the house with a cup of coffee or tea left undrunk? Now you can take it with you in a patented GOJO Mug! GOJO has a clever 'drink-through' insulating lid that stops splashes and keeps the contents hot for up to 30 minutes. The extra-wide non-slip base also helps prevent knockovers, sitting securely on car dashboards or boat decks at up to a 40° slope. Crafted from dishwasher-safe earthenware, GOJO mugs are available in white or smart forest green glaze. ⅓ pint capacity.
GOJO Mug £9.95
White NA23528 **Green** NA22376

The state-of-the-art roasting rack

If you prefer roasting poultry or joints of meat on a rack, this innovative idea is a 'must'. Designed to be placed in a conventional roasting tin, the heavy-gauge non-stick rack is V-shaped so the meat is held securely. When you turn the joint to ensure all-round browning, you can be sure it won't roll back the way it was the moment you reshut the oven door! Below, a full-length non-stick reservoir collects all the delicious juices and drains them to a compartment at one end – making it easy to baste the bird or joint without having to angle the roasting tin or even remove it from the oven. Rack measures approx. 26.6 x 40.6cm (10½" x 16½").

Roasting Rack
£22.95
PA30353

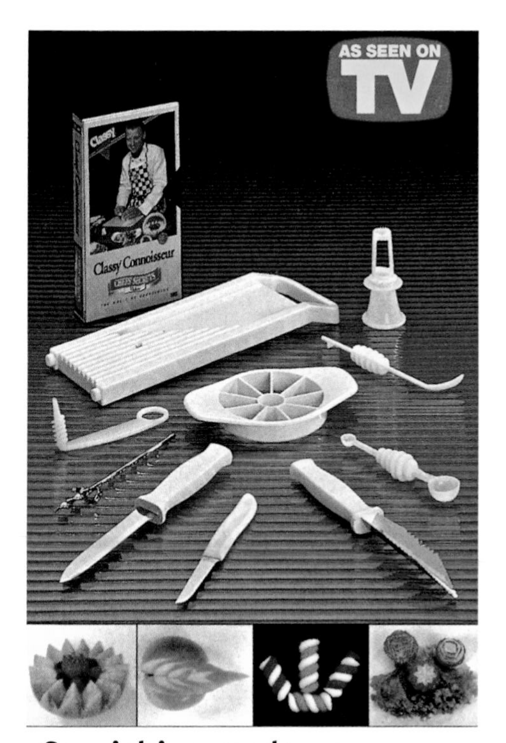

Garnishing made easy

The secret of creating garnish effects is a trick of the chef's trade, not normally revealed to us mere amateurs. However this innovative kit tells all, demonstrating the techniques in a 35-minute instruction video and providing you with ten special tools needed to achieve them. In no time you'll be creating breathtaking garnishes, and your admiring guests will be asking you how it was done . . .

Garnishing Made Easy £14.95 KA33207

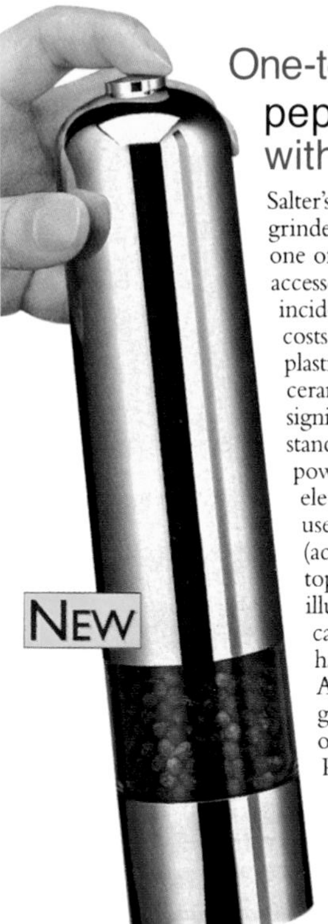

One-touch electric pepper grinder with light

Salter's ultra-stylish new pepper grinder is surely destined to be one of the most desirable table accessories for 1999 - which, incidentally, is exactly what it costs! Within the chromed plastic case is a state-of-the-art ceramic grinding mechanism, significantly harder than a standard metal grinder and powered by a miniature electric motor. For ease of use, operation is one-handed (activated by a button on the top) while a built-in light illuminates your plate so you can see how much pepper has been dispensed. Adjustable for fine or coarse grinding. 5 year guarantee on grinding mechanism. Replacement bulb supplied. Uses 4 x AA batteries (not included).

Electric Pepper Mill
£19.99 MK2676

Teflon-coated Glisdonmes make light of moving

Such a simple idea, but brilliant! Glisdomes are hard rubber discs, coated with ultra-low friction Teflon, that let you move heavy furniture or kitchen appliances effortlessly without castors or back-breaking lifting. Place a Glisdome under each corner and you'll glide even weighty furniture over virtually any floor surface without scratching.

Available in five sizes, each with self-adhesive pads for optional permanent fixing: 20mm diameter for lightweight items such as plant pots or dining chairs; 30mm for TVs, hi-fi units, small beds; 50mm for cookers, fridges, washing machines, armchairs; 60mm for filing cabinets, double beds, wardrobes, dressers etc., 60mm cups for permanent fixture on legs and castors. Also available, the Lifter to help lift heavy objects prior to using Glisdomes.

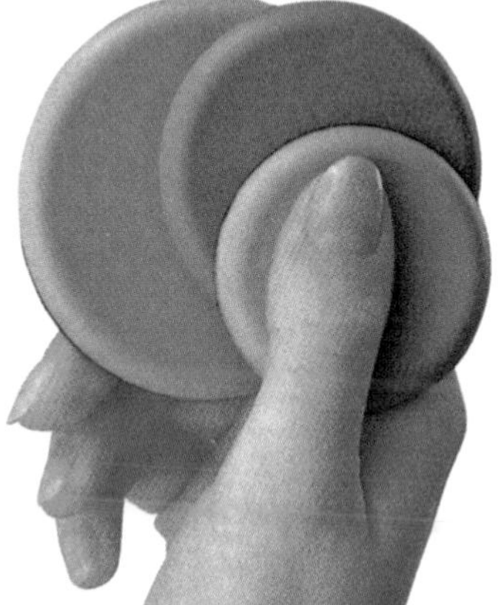

Lifter £14.95 13415
Glisdomes (8 x 20mm) £7.95 13260
Glisdomes (4 x 30mm) £5.95 13261
Glisdomes (4 x 50mm) £8.95 13262
Glisdomes (4 x 60mm) £9.95 13263
Glisdomes (4 x 60mm) cups £16.95 13414

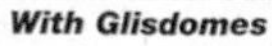

With Glisdomes

Without Glisdomes

new
HOMEDICS
new
Bring the soothing sounds of nature indoors
Followers of Feng Shui believe that water features in a garden can resolve energy blockages - as well as creating a harmonious 'white noise' that blocks out distractions and aids concentration. Now, with these self-contained tabletop fountains, you can bring this relaxing (yet uplifting) concept indoors. The 45.5cm high Water Wave trickles water down the slats of an elegant curved wall, illuminated from below so the effect can also be enjoyed by night. In the 19.5cm Rock Garden, water cascades down layers of slate onto a bed of polished pebbles in the decorative base. Each slate revolves around its centre so the fountain can be customised to create optimum sound and flow. Both designs have mains-powered water pumps with 4 flow speeds so you can select the pace to suit your mood.
Water Wave £79.99 MV1187 Rock Garden £39.99 MV1185

Keep your shoes smelling fresh every day

New shoes smell great but, from the first time you wear them, it's all downhill! Feet create a lot of perspiration creating a moist breeding ground for odour-causing microbes. But with the new Ionic Shoe Freshener™ you can defeat this problem. After each wearing, slip the device into your shoes and switch on. The fanless technology silently draws in fresh air along with freshening negative ions. The air removes the moisture while the ozone destroys the odours at their source. When freshening is complete (around 6 hours), the unit shuts off automatically. Uses 4 x C batteries (not included) or mains adaptor. Measures 21.5 x 14 x 7cm.

Ionic Shoe Freshener™	**£69.99**	MR0045
Mains Adaptor	**£7.99**	MR0421

INNOVATIONS
THE • REPORT
MAY - SEPTEMBER 19
INNOVATIONS
nnis Pal
e page 13
Powerwalk
– see page 8
wing Guider
e page 34
Tsubo Massager
– see page 29
ONE
FITNESS TRAINER
HIT PEAK FITNESS IN 20 MINUTES A DAY FOR 20 DAYS
Dave Baptiste
Zara Long

Introducing improved MC² PLUS – only £169.95

Now available in an advanced new version called MC² PLUS, the amazing Mind Machine claims to help you achieve deep relaxation, accelerate learning and sharpen your thinking - claims endorsed by users worldwide. Simply put on the stereo headphones and the light-producing glasses, and select one of the preset options. Gentle pulses of synchronised light and sound then help you enter the Theta state of relaxation, said to aid super-learning, creativity and problem-solving. MC² PLUS's new features include: Voice Command Key that voice-lists the 10 programmes • All-new keypad to control light intensity, volume, balance and pitch of tone • Extend Key for 5 extra minutes of any sequence • Twin output for 2-person use • Smart carry case • Runs on 2 AA batteries or mains adaptor (not supplied). Also available: three Bright Images subliminal tapes from Canada designed to enhance the MC² experience - Weight Loss/Maintenance, Stop Smoking and Total Relaxation.

MC² PLUS £169.95 FP873
Subliminal Tapes (each) £9.95 Weight Loss/Maintenance FP874 **Stop Smoking** FP875 **Total Relaxation** FP876

Electronic Pillbox with its own water supply!

You may already have seen pill boxes with built-in alarms – they're the best way of reminding you to take medication regularly. But the Aqua PillTimer goes one better! Not only does it have a programmable electronic beeper and a drawer for your pills, it also has an integral water supply. No more hunting for a glass, tap or drinking fountain - just flip open the top and there's a neat little straw leading to the water reservoir. Only 4¼" x 2½", Aqua PillTimer is compact enough to carry in pocket, handbag or briefcase. Micro cell battery and instructions included.

Aqua PillTimer £12.95 FP852

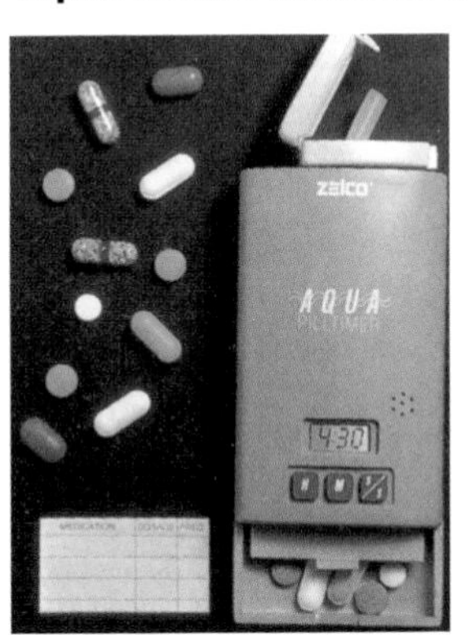

Shape up in the bath!

Devised by physiotherapist Jane Dorey, Bathrobics is a safe new exercise routine that you can do in the comfort and privacy of your bath tub. It's suitable for all ages and all levels of fitness, and requires no equipment other than a bath full of water! Warm up with gentle stretches while the bath is running, then get into the water to firm up buttocks, arms, stomach, hips and thighs. The non-splash exercises use the support and buoyancy of water to assist and resist your muscles. The warmth of the bathwater also helps to minimise risk of strain or injury. Bathrobics pack consists of 10 double-sided waterproof cards, a display stand which sticks to the rim of the bath with a rubber sucker and full instruction booklet.

Bathrobics £14.99 IA17912

Trouser Robe – the more practical bathrobe

Like ordinary robes, these innovative trouser robes are perfect for wicking away moisture and keeping you warm after a bath – but their new jumpsuit styling means they don't gape open or let in draughts, and are much more respectable when guests arrive unexpectedly! Made from machine-washable super-thick 100% cotton towelling, the robes feature tie belt fastening, and a roll up collar that can also be worn as a hood to help dry hair. Choose from 3 generous unisex sizes – S (height 5'–5'5"), M (height 5'5"–5' 9½") and L (5'9½"–6'2"). Please state size required in the size column on your order form.

Trouser Robe £39.99
IA11690

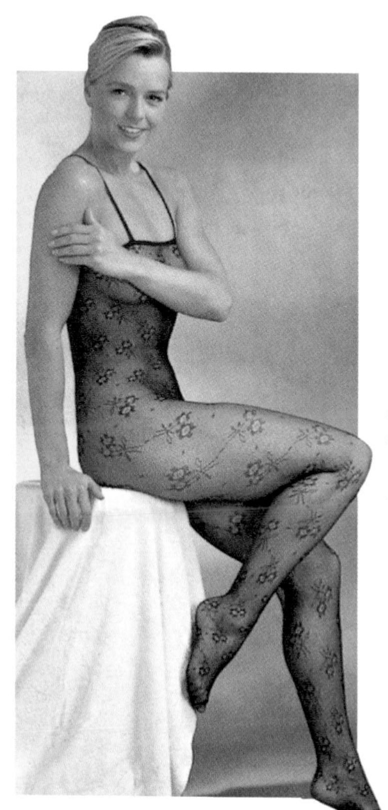

Queentex Lace Bodystocking only £9.99

Inspired by classic French lingerie, the Queentex sheer lacy bodystocking is chic, seductive and very versatile. A combination camisole/pantyhose, it looks great and feels comfortable however you want to wear it: beneath a blouse and skirt, or under a dress, shirt, sweater or jacket. It's wonderfully flattering, hugging the body like a sensual second skin. Made of super-stretchy soft lightweight nylon (one size fits all), the seamless Bodystocking has an open gusset for comfort.

Bodystocking Black
£9.99 WB19965
Bodystocking White
£9.99 WB11696

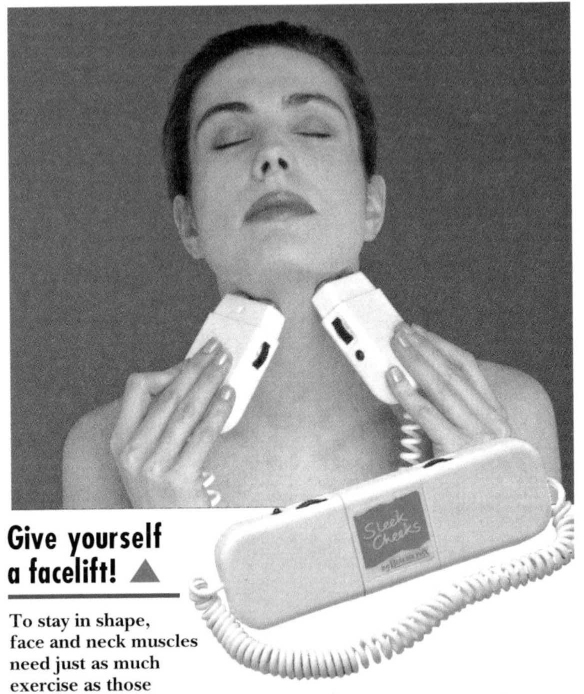

Give yourself a facelift! ▲

To stay in shape, face and neck muscles need just as much exercise as those elsewhere in your body, but they're difficult to train and often neglected. Now you can use the superb British-made Sleek Cheeks exerciser to help fight wrinkles and double chins by helping to lift your facial contours for a healthier, more youthful face. The handsets work by transmitting tiny electrical pulses into the muscles, stimulating muscle contraction, increasing tissue blood supply and nourishing cells in a safe and gentle way. With two handsets, you can give both sides of your face a work-out at the same time. Full instructions and batteries supplied.

Sleek Cheeks £43.50 OB15785

Breakthrough drug-free treatment for migraine pain

There are few pains worse than the awful throbbing ache of a migraine. For many sufferers, nothing really helps to relieve it except for powerful painkilling drugs – which can often have the equally unpleasant side-effect of 'knocking you out'. However, now you can try a safe new product that uses NO drugs and has NO side-effects. The Sea-Band Head-Band (designed by the same people who make those brilliant anti-travel sickness wrist bands) has been developed specifically to help decrease the severity of migraine headaches. It comprises a washable elasticated band which fixes around the head by Velcro, under which you place one or two firm rubber disks to apply localised pressure over the area(s) of maximum pain. This method has long been known to migraine sufferers who have used the pressure of their fingers – but the Sea-Band Head-Band achieves better and more consistent results (and more conveniently) than using finger pressure alone. In clinical trials conducted by an American neurologist, 87% of patients with severe migraine pain, experienced relief using Sea-Band Head-Band.

Sea-Band Head-Band
£12.95 NB20406

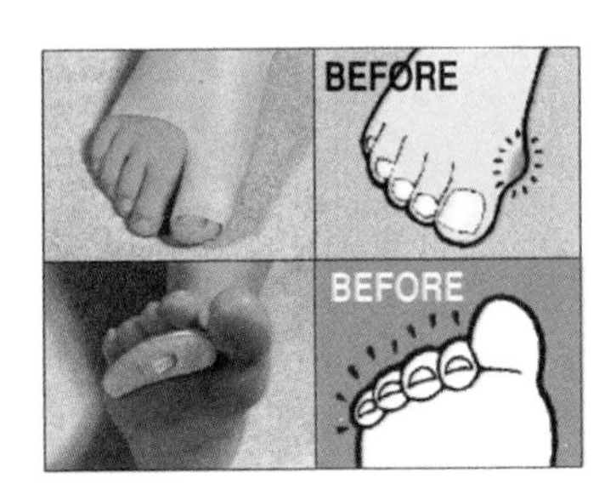

Toe relief ▲

BIG TOE STRAIGHTENER is for sufferers of inclined big toes. Used daily it genuinely helps to re-align your big toe, on either foot, to the correct position. This reduces shoe pressure, so helping to prevent unsightly and painful bunions. Comfortable to wear. TOE RELIEF PADS are for sufferers of claw and hammer toes. These little cushions mould to the correct orthopaedic form of your feet to gently urge toes into a more normal position, relieving pressure and friction.

Toe Straightener £5.95 DC19230
Buy two for £9.95 DA19231
Relief Pad (pair) £5.95 DB18911
Two pairs £9.95 DA18912

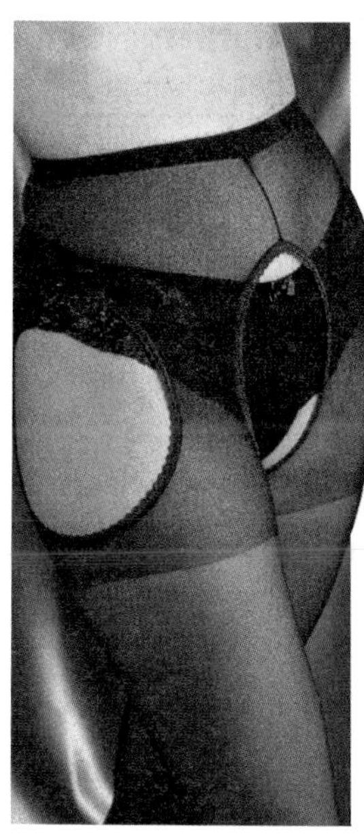

Glamour Suspender Stockings

Fashionable, hygienic and sensual – the new stockings with built-in suspenders that you put on and take off like tights. As convenient as tights, as glamorous as stockings. Air is allowed to circulate making you feel cool, comfortable and sexy.

Please state colour – Barely Black, Mink or Honey, and size required – Standard, up to 107cm (42") hip or Large, 114-137cm (45"-54") hip on order form.

Glamour Stockings 3 pair pack £9.95
DA18787

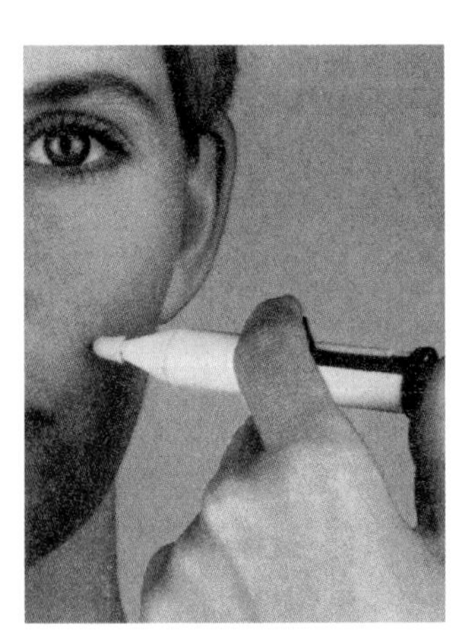

Pore Cleaner ▼

This simple hand-held vacuum action pump helps remove blackheads from beneath the surface of your skin, quickly, painlessly and without bruising, to leave a smoother, clearer complexion. Ideal for combination skin without drying or damaging delicate areas. Made from easy-clean hygienic plastic.

Pore Cleaner £5.95 DD19206

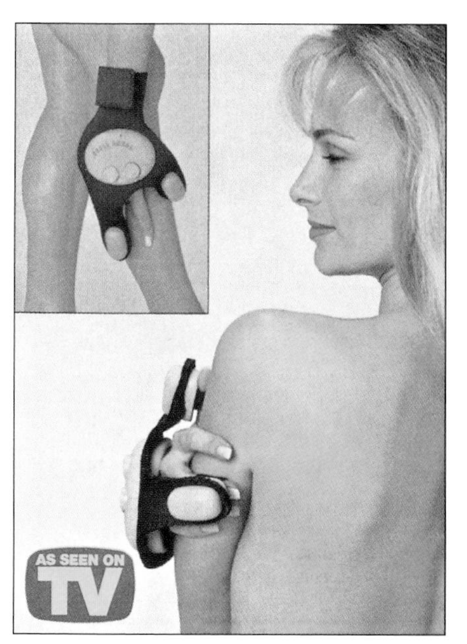

Professional 'fingertip-therapy' massage glove

The Tsubo Glove adds a touch of modern technology to the ancient art of fingertip massage. Comfortable and easy to use, the electrically-powered Tsubo Glove is worn on the right hand to provide a massage experience like never before – administered either by yourself or by a partner. Dual oscillating motors in the two fingertip pods – each independently controllable for speed and intensity – deliver relaxing, therapeutic massage to virtually any part of the body: on the temples, scalp and neck to help ease headaches; on the shoulders and upper and lower back to help aching muscles 'unwind' after a stressful day; on the arms and legs to reduce the pain of specific sports injuries. Tsubo is made from durable neoprene fabric with an adjustable wrist strap and variable-sized rings to ensure perfect fit for every user. Better still, its power source is built-in. The glove contains a rechargeable NiCad battery pack that provides 20 minutes' fully cordless massage on full power. If you require a longer massage, the recharger unit (supplied) can be used as a mains transformer for continuous corded operation.

Tsubo Glove £49.95 PA28598

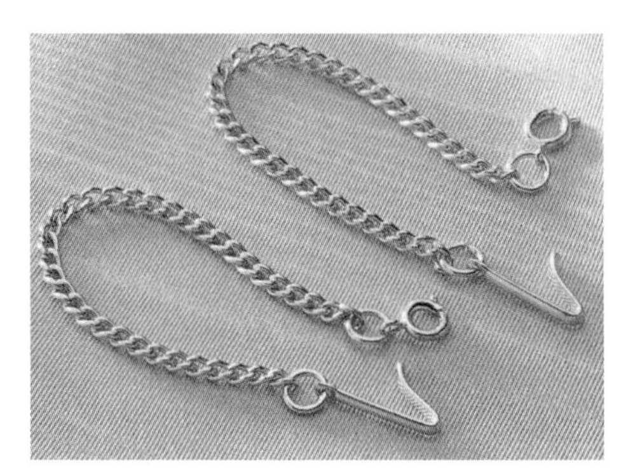

Necklace too short? Then extend it!

If you've got a favourite necklace that's just a little too tight for comfort, this simple American idea provides the instant solution. These discreet extension chains fasten onto any necklace with a hook and jump ring, immediately adding approx 12.5cms (5") to the length. They're also a great way to vary the length of existing necklaces to suit your outfit. Pack of two in gold and silver tones.
Necklace Extenders £7.95 PA28717

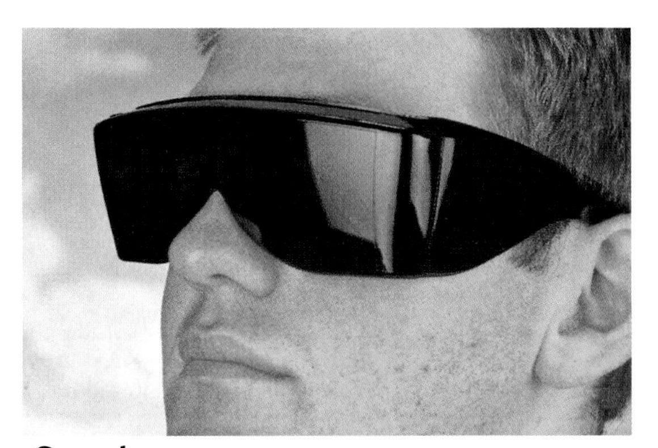

Sunglasses you wear over normal specs

If you wear glasses, combating bright sunlight has always meant one of two solutions – either irritating clip-ons or costly prescription sunglasses. Now there's a third option in the shape of Eliminator wrap-arounds. These smart sunglasses are designed to be worn over regular corrective specs, preventing the ingress of harsh sunlight from any angle and eliminating 100% of the sun's harmful rays.
Eliminator Sunglasses £8.95
PA31105

Give yourself 'eagle' eyesight

The eagle has the best vision of all living creatures because its eyes contain a unique oil that gives the bird total immunity from the damaging glare of brilliant sunlight. EagleEyes® Sunglasses are science's attempt to replicate this amazing optical gift, giving you sharper, clearer vision and protecting your retinas from stress and sun damage. The polarised lenses block 100% of UVA, UVB and UVC rays, cutting glare and haze, enhancing natural colours. And if all these benefits are not enough, £19.95 also buys you a pair of ultra-fashionable lightweight shatter-proof sunglasses complete with smart aluminium case.

EagleEyes £19.95 KA33296

Firm up sagging mattresses

Whether you're at home, on holiday, in a hotel or staying over with friends or relatives, now you can ensure a better night's sleep whatever the deficiencies of the mattress. Simply unfold this ½" thick bedboard and slide it between the mattress and base of the bed for instant support and comfort. Made of sturdy 7-ply air cushion board that's half the weight of a conventional wooden bedboard and easily transportable when travelling. Available in two widths (24" or 30"), the board measures 60" long and the smaller size folds down to just 15". For double beds, order two.

Folding Mattress Support
(24") £16.95 NA25689 **(30") £18.95** NA25690

The Gemini Skin System

Independent dermatological clinical trials have demonstrated that the Gemini System can increase the elasticity of the skin on treated areas. This exciting new UK-made device uses a process call Galvanic Iontophoresis, employed in professional salons for many years. In simple terms, this means creating a flow of ions through the skin from a negative pad to a positive pad. Gemini uses the process to draw the essential oils and other active ingredients in the Aromesque Ionising Gel Therapie through the skin and fatty tissues below the surface. By stimulating the metabolism, Gemini encourages the flushing of excess fluid and toxins from fatty subcutaneous deposits, and disperses them towards the major lymph nodes where they are disposed of naturally. Kit includes 100ml Gel Therapie and 4 special pads and sponges in a neat travel case. Powered by single PP3 battery (not supplied) and free instruction video included.

Gemini Skin System £69 KA30769

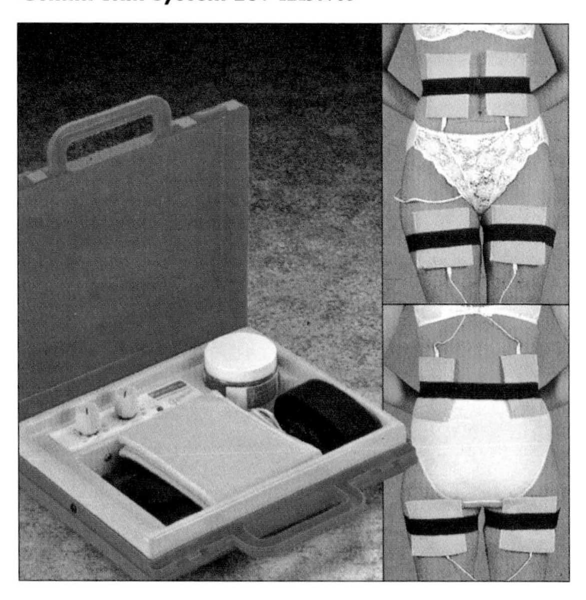

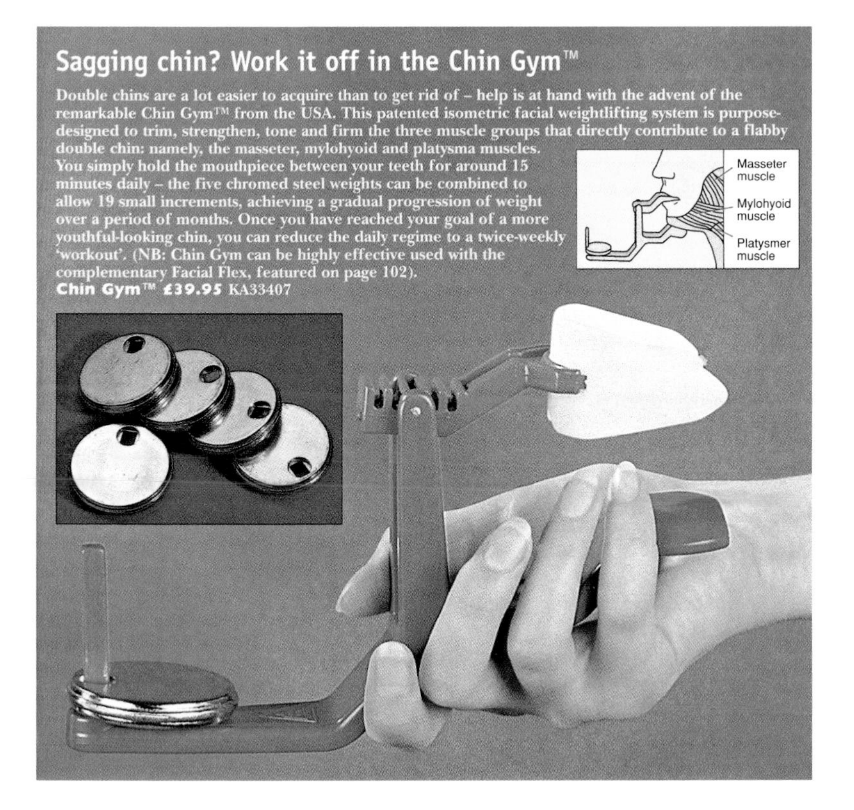
Sagging chin? Work it off in the Chin Gym™
Double chins are a lot easier to acquire than to get rid of – help is at hand with the advent of the remarkable Chin Gym™ from the USA. This patented isometric facial weightlifting system is purpose-designed to trim, strengthen, tone and firm the three muscle groups that directly contribute to a flabby double chin: namely, the masseter, mylohyoid and platysma muscles. You simply hold the mouthpiece between your teeth for around 15 minutes daily – the five chromed steel weights can be combined to allow 19 small increments, achieving a gradual progression of weight over a period of months. Once you have reached your goal of a more youthful-looking chin, you can reduce the daily regime to a twice-weekly 'workout'. (NB: Chin Gym can be highly effective used with the complementary Facial Flex, featured on page 102).
Chin Gym™ £39.95 KA33407
Masseter muscle
Mylohyoid muscle
Platysmer muscle

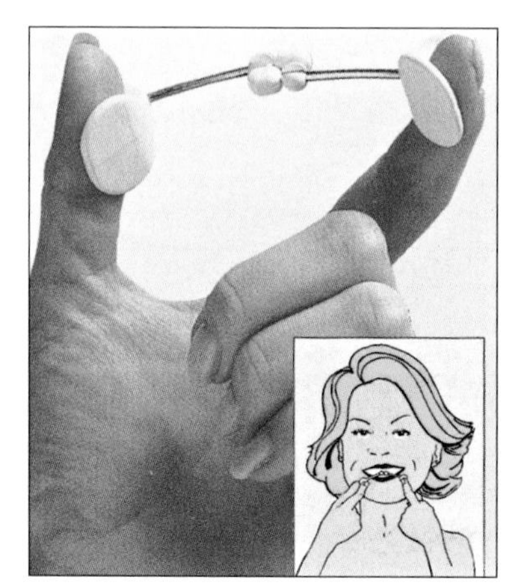

A unique exercise machine for 'facial fitness'

Underlying your facial skin is a complex muscular system. When these muscles lose strength and tone, the skin becomes loose and saggy around the eyes, mouth, jawline and neck – and this is when some people turn to cosmetic surgery. But now, with the revolutionary Facial Flex®, you have an effective and easy alternative. First developed for stroke rehabilitation, Facial Flex® does for your face what regular workouts do for your body. An ultra-lightweight device, precision-made from surgical stainless steel and ABS plastic with dental-grade elastic resistance, it locates comfortably in the corners of the mouth. Using only your facial muscles, compress and release it 40-60 times per minute for about two minutes against the dynamic resistance of the elastic band. A trial in the USA showed amazing results: in just two months, subjects achieved an average 32% increase in facial firmness and 250% increase in facial muscle strength. Facial Flex® measures 2"across, weighs 10oz.
Facial Flex® £49.95 NA23525

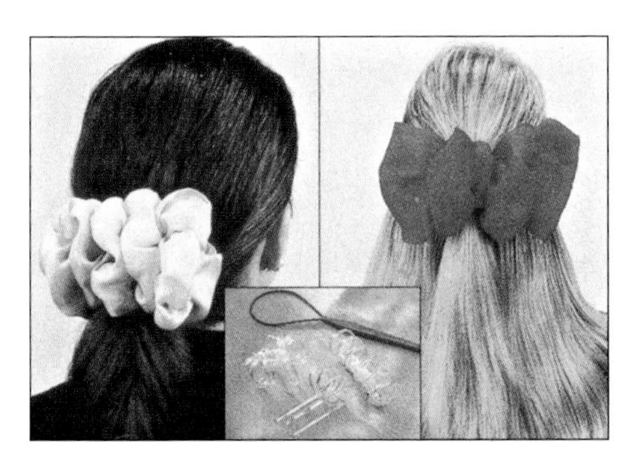

Turn any scarf or fabric into a beautiful hair bow

Have you got a drawer full of scarves you hardly ever wear? Then discover Bowrette, a sensational new way to design and create dozens of fabulous one-off bows and accessories for the hair. It's easy to use and takes seconds – and when you're bored with a bow, just pull out the scarf and start again! You can also turn left-over fabric into a bow to co-ordinate with your outfit, or create a whole new look with ties, scrunchies, ribbons, (even shoe laces!) without sewing or gluing. Teenagers love Bowrette too; they'll have fun making inexpensive hair bows to match their favourite outfits. Kit comprises 3 Bowrettes (Barrette, Clip & Pin) plus styling tool and 18-page styling booklet.

Bowrette Collection £14.95 PA29127

Professional braids in minutes

Create beautiful, professional salon-style French braids with the ingenious Braid Master, which acts like an extra pair of hands. Use the special foam-grip 'combs' to hold your hair while you follow the video's simple step-by-step instructions to create your favourite hair styles.

Pair of Braid Masters & Video £9.95 KA31047

Pair of Braid Masters £4.95 KA31048

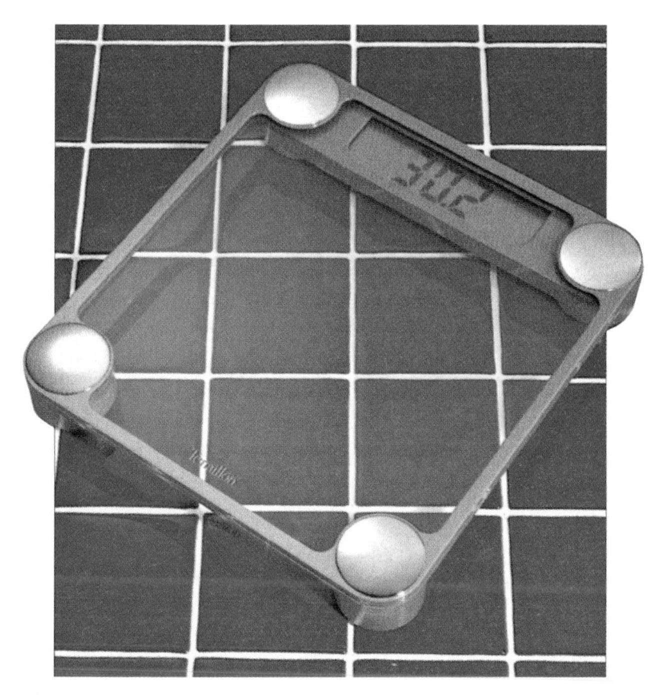

Bathroom scale or work of art?

Here's a masterpiece of modern sculptural art, designed not for your living room wall but for your bathroom floor! Created around a 29 x 31cm (11½" x 12") sheet of toughened glass, the state-of-the-art IKON scale offers stunning looks, technical innovation and exceptional accuracy. Operation is completely automatic – simply step on and your weight is displayed in metric or imperial on the large 25mm (1") LCD readout. So how does it work? Concealed in each of the four 'feet' is an active high-precision sensor that makes the IKON accurate within +/–0.3% of total body weight, with clever technology that 'locks in' the reading only when your position on the scale is fully stabilised. Supplied with 2 standard batteries for approx. 10 years' use before replacing.

IKON Glass Scale £99.00 KA32802

Wash your back without stretching, your feet without bending

Whether you stand in the shower or sit in the bath, this clever idea helps you get your back and feet really clean without the twisting ability of a contortionist or having to balance on one leg! Using the powerful suction pads, attach BrushClean to your bath or tiled shower. Now simply apply your favourite soap and scrub those hard to reach parts by rubbing against the special brush fibres - no less than 35,000 of them. The bacteria free filaments made from a polypropylene that retains its stiffness in hot or cold water, and resists mildew, alkalies, acids etc. Why not buy a pair (one for your feet, the other for your back) and make a saving? Each measures 23 x 16cm (9" x 6").

BrushClean (each) **£9.99** MK2614
(two) **£18.99** MK2681

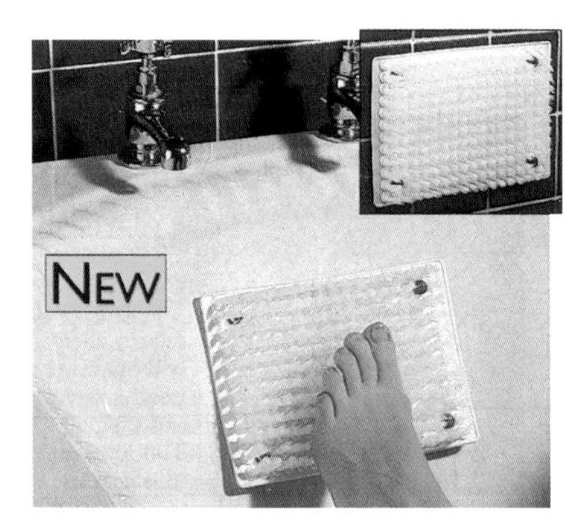

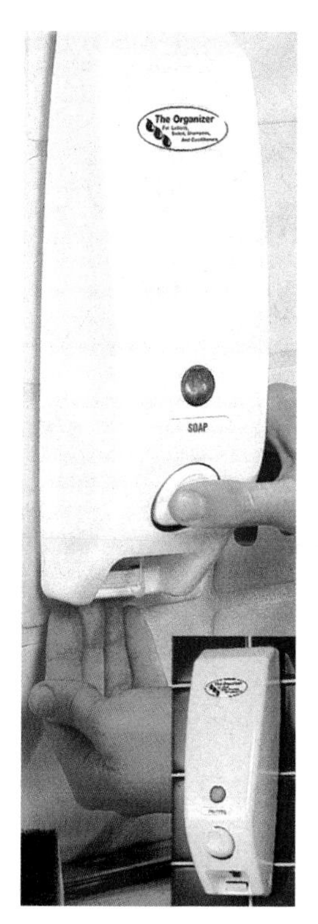

Hassle-free way to dispense soap and shampoo

Say goodbye to all those bottles of shampoo, conditioner and shower gel that clutter up your bathroom. This space-saving dispenser fixes with self-adhesive pads or hooks (not supplied) beside the shower or by the sink, and at the touch of a button it delivers a contolled measure straight into your hand. Suitable for shampoo, conditioner or liquid soap. Used by the sink in the kitchen it avoids messy washing-up liquid bottles. Measures 8.5 x 27 x 8cm (3½" x 10½" x 3")

Shower Dispenser
£9.99 MK2373
Shower Dispenser (pack of 2)
£17.99 MK2525

Soft fleecy snuggler suit – for grownups
If you've ever envied babies the comfort and warmth of their all-in-one suits, here's one for adults! The ultimate cuddler, it's just perfect for curling up and hibernating at home with a book or video on long wet and chilly evenings. Made from soft fleece fabric, the suit is roomy, snug and very comfortable with a zip front, elasticised ankle and wrist. Machine washable. Available in S/M or L/XL in either burgundy, navy, cherry red or hunter green; please state size and colour required when ordering.
Fleece Snuggler Suit
£44.99 MR1582
Navy
Humter Green
Cherry red

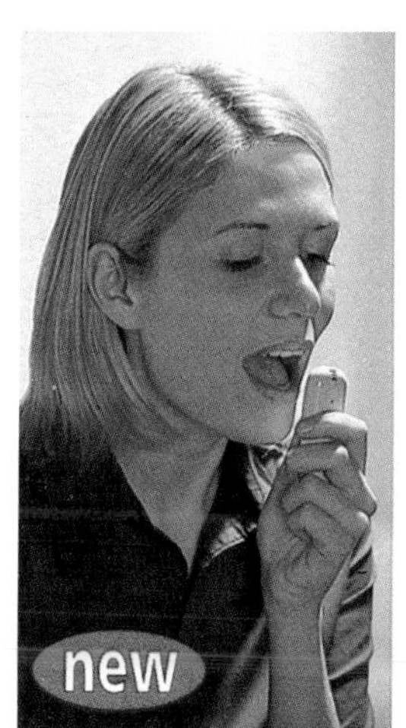

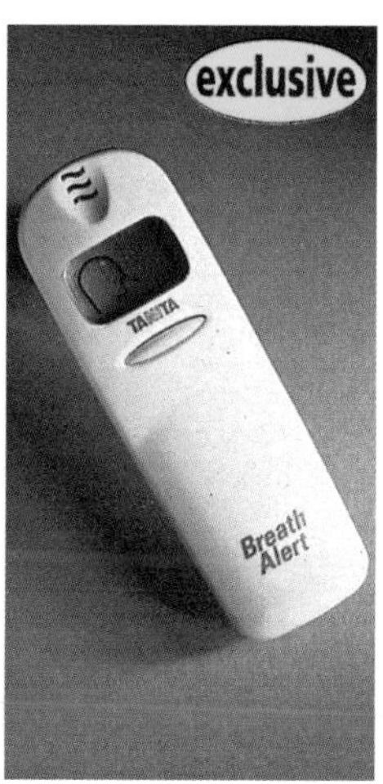

Check your breath is really fresh

Ever have the sneaking suspicion your breath isn't quite as fresh as you'd want? Then this little device is a discreet way to check. Simply breathe onto the tiny gas sensor and after 5 seconds, BreathAlert gives a guide in four grades (from None to Strong) so you can take action if necessary. Small enough for pocket or purse. Requires 2 x AAA batteries (supplied).

BreathAlert **£19.99** MV1215

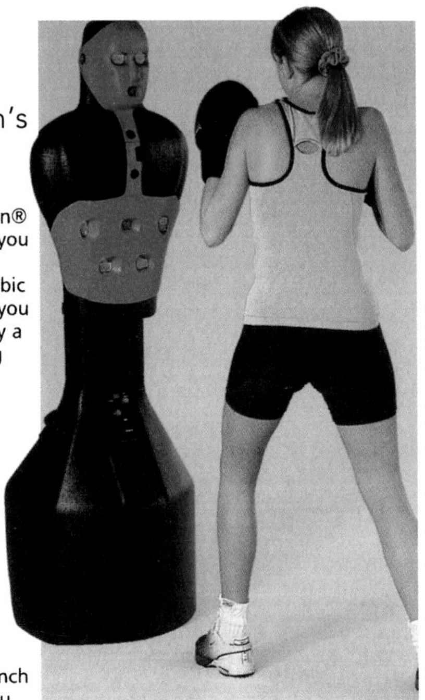

Can you punch SlamMan's lights out?

With SlamMan® not only can you benefit from effective aerobic exercise, but you can also enjoy a stress-busting session of aggressive boxing! SlamMan® is incredibly tough. His striking surfaces are made from ultra-dense moulded foam with memory retention. Punch as hard as you can, and he always returns to shape. To sharpen up your reflexes and co-ordination, SlamMan® tells you when and where to hit him. His 8 target LEDs are programmed to light up in challenging sequences (adjustable strike sensors means you have to hit harder to make each light go out). Computer features 3 combat levels, 5 boxing programs and random program for the ultimate challenge. Comes with universal-fit gloves, 'how to' video and boxer's eating plan. Uses 2 x AAA batteries (not supplied). **NB: fill base with 240lbs dry sand (not supplied) for total stability. Free delivery with this product.**

new

SlamMan® **£299.00** MG1893

Wear your genius for all to see!
Albert Einstein and Sigmund Freud – two of the 20th century's most dynamic thinkers – are portrayed, somewhat irreverently, on these 100% cotton T-shirts. Available in one size – extra large. Machine washable.
Freud T-shirt £12.95 AA436
Einstein T-shirt £12.95 AA435
Albert Einstein
Sigmund Freud

INNOVATION
H E · R E P O R
Sp
E WIRELESS
TERCOM DOORCHIME
atest development in the
of radio waves, designed in
own technical department.
INNOVATIO
OMAS EDISON (1847-1931)
on's invention of the first incandescent
bulb revealed 'the Edison effect', later

Magnetic Video Titling Kit

This compact attaché case contains everything needed to create attractive titles and captions for your video productions – at a fraction of the cost of electronic titlers. Simply arrange the magnetic characters onto the double-sided background (using one of the three decorative overlays for an extra creative effect) then commit the finished title screen directly to videotape using your camcorder. Kit comprises: metal title board, 129 magnetic characters, 3 overlays, T-square to ensure accurately lined-up type.
Magnetic Titling Kit £39.99 WB18197

LavaBuns, the 8-hour heated cushion

A revolutionary idea from the USA, the LavaBuns Heated Seat Cushion retains warmth for up to 8 hours! Simply microwave it for five minutes and you've got a really comfortable heated seat to use any time the weather gets cold – when you're watching sports, fishing, driving or even at home. Moreover, it's great as a heated back support cushion and can also be chilled to provide cold relief for aches and sprains. Lightweight and durable, the LavaBuns Heated Seat Cushion has a smart Teflon-treated Dupont cover that resists stains and water and the whole thing folds up into a compact case. Cushion measures 13" x 2" opened and 7" x 11" folded.
LavaBuns Heated Seat Cushion £37.50 WA20946

Party time with Magic Mic

With four hilarious SFX at your fingertips, the Goodmans Magic Mic is great fun for performers of all ages! The Voice Changer function permits you to vary your speaking (or singing) voice from a Darth Vader soundalike to one of the Chipmunks! The Drum Sound lets you rap along to a funky beat on the drum pads. The built-in Laughter Soundtrack means you can be sure *someone* will respond to your comic turn – and finally you can call up realistic Audience Applause! Plugs into any audio device with a microphone input (eg PA amp, karaoke, tape recorder, hi-fi system). Also works as conventional microphone. Uses 4 x AAA batteries (not supplied).
Magic Mic £39.95 NB22926

Electronic fishing with action-packed surprises

You've never played an electronic game quite like this! Lake Trout Fishin' mixes skill-based LCD action with realistic physical exertion. Start by choosing your lake, boat location and lure. Then, holding down the CAST button, simulate the action of casting. Now gently reel in the lure with the mechanical handle . . . and if you're skilful enough, a trout will strike. Pull back to set the hook and the serious action begins. As if you were holding a real rod, the game shakes in your hand while you try to reel him in. Includes Weekend Fishing and Tournament Options, Best Catch Records and more. 2 x AA batteries supplied.

Lake Trout Fishin'
£24.95
KA33460

"Take your partner . . . and learn country dancing!"

American country dancing is sweeping the world – and after learning the basic moves from these videos you'll feel comfortable about getting off your chair and joining in the fun. Unlike some other dance videos that leave you to practise on your own, Diane Horner takes you through the steps until they become automatic. In Country Line Dancing you'll learn simple moves common to many dances, then discover the basics of partner dancing – footwork, simple turns, the promenade position and the 'cuddle'. Now that you can do the basic steps, More Country Line Dancing goes on to increase your repertoire. Each dance is broken down into patterns, making it fun and easy to practise.

Country Line Dancing £12.95 KA33320
More Country Line Dancing £12.95 KA33321

Learn to jive from the experts

Modern jive appeals to people of all tastes and ages, not just committed rock'n'rollers! It can be danced to just about any music – and it's also surprisingly easy to learn from this 56-minute video. With great music from The Firebirds, the video intersperses easy-to-follow instructional sections with breathtaking jive sequences performed by professional champions. You'll be patiently guided through over 20 individual moves then shown how to put them together into a routine that will amaze your friends!
Jive Video £13.95 KA28294

new
exclusive
MOON LAND
LUNAR CONSTITUTION
BILL OF RIGHTS
LUNAR MAP
LUNAR DEED
Land on the Moon!
Your chance to own an acre of Moon (honestly!)
The Outer Space Treaty of 1967 decreed that no country could lay claim to the Moon. But it forgot to say that no individual could do so! So in 1980 an American called Dennis M. Hope legally claimed the entire Moon, filing his claim with the US and USSR governments and the UN General Assembly. Now for just £19.99 you can legally buy one acre of the moon's surface. You get a Lunar Deed of Ownership with the exact co-ordinates of your plot, a lunar map showing the location, the Lunar Constitution, transcript of the original 1980 Declaration of Ownership plus a document confirming your Mineral Rights to your acre. It's somewhat tongue-in-cheek – but all totally legal and above board!
Acre of Moon £19.99 MG6665

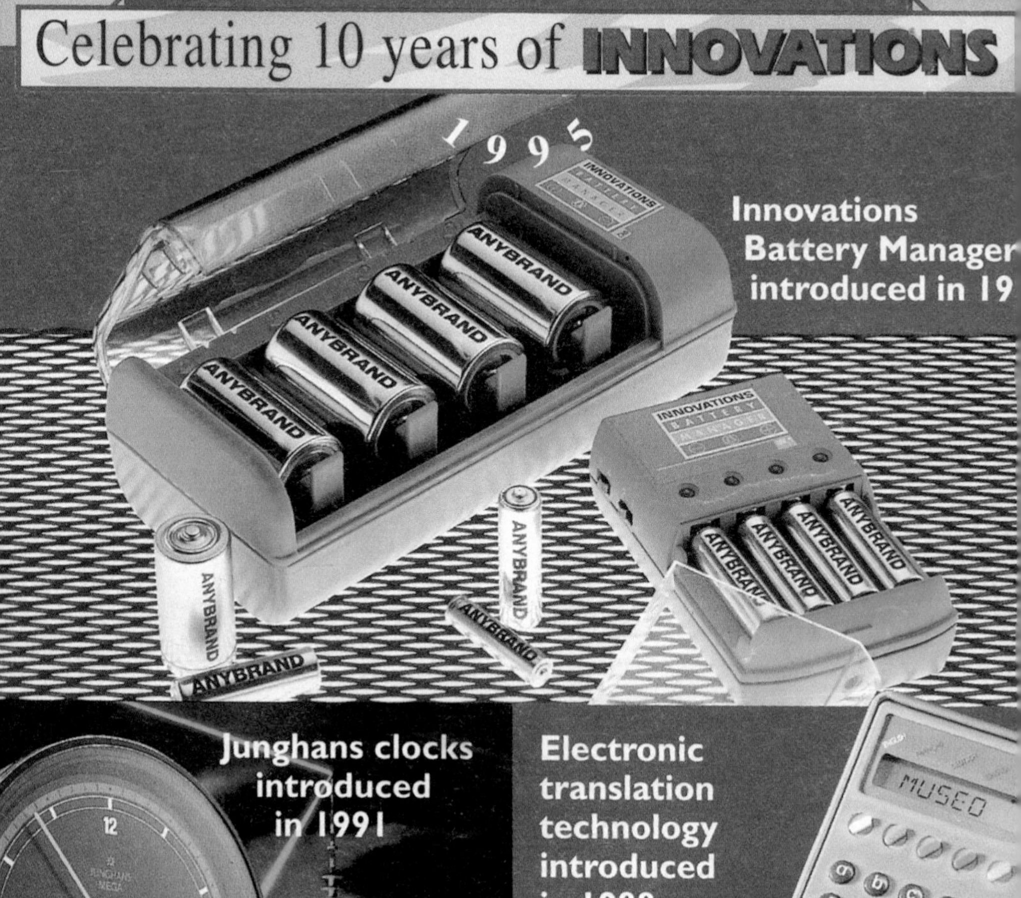

Electronic
translation
technology
introduced
in 1988

World's first fully-portable electronic routefinder
Columbus is a unique hand-held computer capable of planning any UK road journey in seconds! You enter your starting point (or current position) and destination, and Columbus swiftly calculates the rest, based on the quickest or most economical route. On request, it can even plan routes avoiding cities, built-up areas, low bridges or toll roads! As you travel, simply consult the illuminated LCD screen for clear step-by-step text instructions for your journey. Just as valuable is the Traffic Re-Route function; if you hit road works or traffic, the computer can instantly work out an alternative route to minimise queueing or delay. Columbus also monitors every aspect of your trip, saving you time and money. It gives your ETA (estimated time of arrival) and can update this data throughout the journey. It tells you the mileage between any two given points, calculates your travel costs for business and expense planning, and can organise up to five separate destinations into the most efficient order. Other features include an on-screen Compass Display, indicating direction of travel at junctions, and a 'Hotkey Information' function that gives detailed local directions (eg: 'second exit at roundabout' or 'right at The Red Lion public house'). Columbus comes with the AA's entire GB database on a slot-in 16 MB card containing nearly 12,000 major locations, 27,000 smaller towns and villages, plus a total of over 40,000 roads! Powered by 4 x AA batteries (not supplied), Columbus measures 4 ½" x 7 ¾" x ¾". Recommended by the AA.
Columbus RouteFinder/GB data card £399.50 IA17625
COLUMBUS

Parking without tears!

Bumpstop is a 100% effective solution to an age-old parking problem. Namely, knowing when to stop before you dent or scratch your car on the back wall of your garage. Place the Bumpstop a safe distance in front of the wall or workshop area. Whether going in forwards or reversing, when your bumper touches the lightweight plastic pole the 'STOP' sign quivers, telling you to go no further. Freestanding and portable, Bumpstop is 48" high, making it clearly visible from the inside of the vehicle.

Bumpstop £19.99
IA17458

Clamp your own car?

When a car is clamped, its pretty well immobilised. This is why the police use clamps on illegally-parked vehicles. But it also means (when used by the private motorist) the dreaded wheel clamp makes a superbly effective security device! The Dezac Wheel Clamp is made from strong steel, secures in seconds with a tough all-weather padlock, and comes with this reassuring guarantee: Dezac will underwrite your insurance policy for up to £250 if the vehicle is stolen when the clamp is properly fitted. Clamp made in UK.

Dezac Wheel Clamp £44.99 IA17486

Aircraft Technology puts you on the right track

This state-of-the-art Electronic Car Compass uses flux-gate sensing as employed on aeroplanes to provide accurate flat screen viewing of the direction in which you are travelling. You need never be driving the wrong way down the right road again, and because the display is also illuminated, it's easy to read both day and night. 3" x 3¾" x 2". Supplied with mounting bracket and adaptor for cigarette lighter socket.
Electronic Car Compass £49.99 WC19056

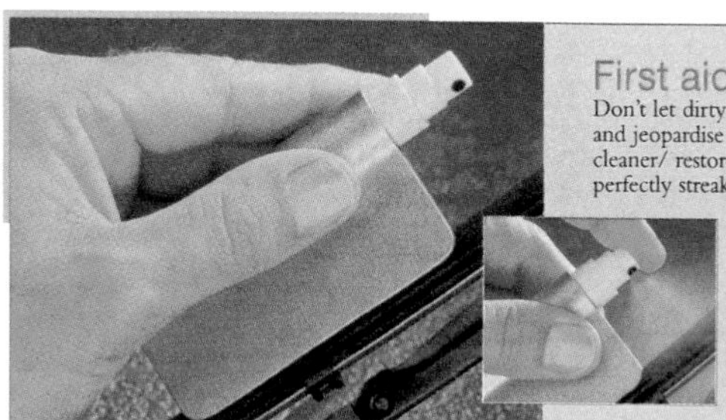

First aid for dirty wipers

Don't let dirty wiper blades reduce driver visibility and jeopardise your safety. This compact all-in-one cleaner/ restorer wipes away dirt and grit, ensuring a perfectly streak-free windscreen and preserving the life of the blades. It features an abrasive edge to keep the blades smooth, plus a built-in pump spray to squirt off dirt and road grime. Includes 5 abrasive sheet refills. 10 x 4.5 x 1cm (4½" x 2" x 1")

Wiper Blade Restorer

£9.99 MK2387

NNOVATION
Tomorrow's Products Today
Kitchen
Garden
Outdoors
Duracraft

Take your cat out for walkies!

Most cats like to follow their owners around the house. The truth is, many cats might really enjoy joining you for a walk if given the chance! This specially-designed 50ft leather leash and body halter is the safest way to do so; unlike a dog's lead and collar it won't place strain on the more delicate feline neck. Just £9.99 – go on, give it a try! Your cat could absolutely love it.
Cat Leash/Harness £9.99 IA17599

FIVE ADJUSTABLE SIZES
XS S M L XL
17"/43cm 24"/60cm 30"/75cm 36"/90cm 42"/106cm
Sizes refer to maximum chest circumference

Give your dog the protection you give yourself

There are plenty of good reasons to restrain a dog in the car – to control a nervous or lively animal, to prevent it distracting the driver, to stop it escaping. But most of all, to protect the dog (and its fellow passengers) in the event of an accident or heavy braking. Now, for £15.95 or less, you can achieve all these objectives. This anatomically-correct Dog Safety Harness clips instantly onto a rear seatbelt, allowing your pet the freedom to sit, lie and turn. Meanwhile, the arrangement of strong belts and extra-wide front piece are specially designed to absorb the animal's weight in the event of a sudden stop. Available in five adjustable sizes (see chart). NB: XS does not have padded front piece. Made in UK.

Dog Safety Harness XS £10.95 NA26172
Small £12.95 NA26173 **Large £13.95** NA26175
Medium £13.75 NA26174 **XL £15.95** NA26176

Pet feeding as regular as clockwork

Unlike battery-powered models, this new automatic pet feeder from leading manufacturer Staywell runs on a simpler and cheaper clockwork action. It can be set to deliver up to six wet or dry meals over a period of 36 hours - ideal for feeding your cat (or even a small dog) while you have to be away. Measuring 11½" diameter and made from easy-clean, dishwasher-safe plastic, the bowl itself is also ideal for everyday use.

Clockwork Pet Feeder
£13.95 EE853

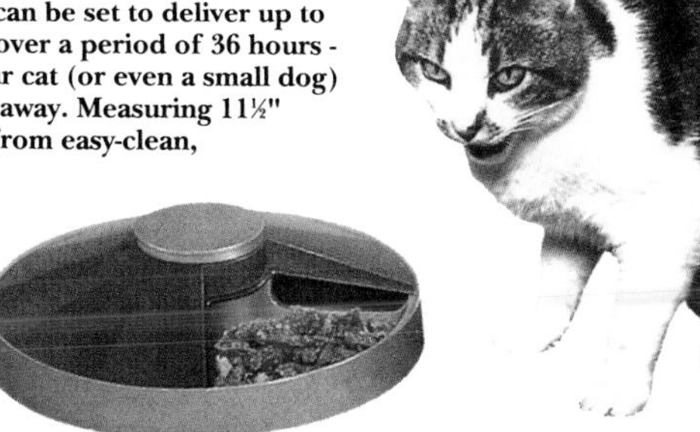

A safe, heated haven for your pet

Previously supplied only to vets, kennels and catteries, these professional-quality Heated Pet Beds provide genuinely safe, economical warmth for dogs or cats. Now also available direct to Innovations customers, the beds are made of tough hygienic plastic with an advanced carbon-film heating element sealed into the base. A built-in thermostatic control restricts heat output to a safe maximum of 45° C. Powered from the mains, the running costs are very low. The 21" bed, for cats and small dogs, costs less than 5p per 24 hours; the 30" version, for medium to large dogs, costs under 10p for each 24 hours. Supplied with 6' mains-cable, armoured with Metaflex to withstand chewing or damage. NB: thick cushions and pet quilts are not required for lining the beds; they will merely insulate your pet from the warmth. An ordinary blanket is enough.
Small Heated Pet Bed £49.95 EE861
Large Heated Pet Bed £59.95 EE862

'Early warning' healthcare kit for pets

The sooner an ailment is identified the easier it is to be cured, saving you time and money, and minimising pain and suffering for your pet. Although nothing should take the place of treatment from a qualified vet, with the right equipment and basic know-how it can be easy for dog and cat owners to detect many common conditions in their early stages. This 'ear, nose and eye' kit gives you everything needed to identify infections and other problems. Firstly, a professionally-written 16-page booklet on how to conduct examination procedures and how to recognise problems such as ear mites, wax accumulation, gum disease, tartar build-up, cataracts and many more; and secondly, the Examlight with high-power integral illumination, four different types of speculum attachments and high-quality magnifying lens.
Uses 4 x AAA batteries, supplied.
Pet Examination Kit £29.95 KA32775

Pet Vac — electronic pet grooming

Pet Vac is the more effective way to groom cats and dogs. Battery-operated, it incorporates a powerful mini fan to vacuum up hair and loose dirt as you brush, helping to keep your pet's coat clean and free of troublesome hair balls. It's quick and almost silent, so your pet should stay calm and comfortable at all times, yet it's also powerful enough to remove fleas and eggs. Choose Pet Vac for dogs (4 x CC batteries, not included), and smaller Pet Vac II for cats (2 x CC batteries, not included). Both models are lightweight and cordless for easy operation, feature easy-empty collection chamber and non-abrasive nylon brushes.

Dog Pet Vac £19.95 EE706A
Cat Pet Vac II £14.95 EE705A

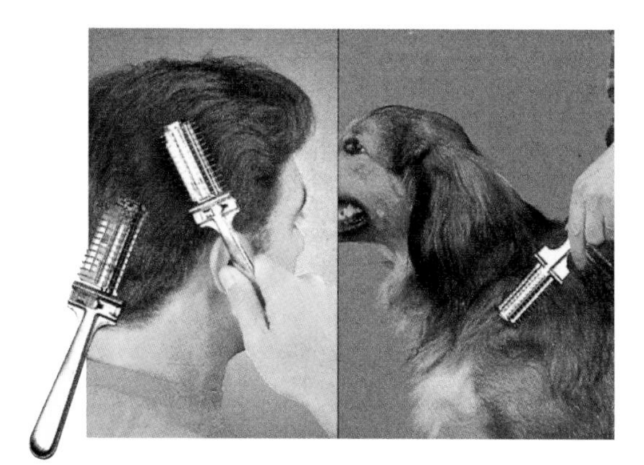

Professional grooming at home, in minutes 

Save a fortune on hairdressing bills with new Trim & Cut. A choice of three blade settings give a neat trim to hair or beards in a matter of minutes, in the comfort of your own home. Can be used on all hair textures, wet or dry, and has a no-cut setting so you can use the steel comb to groom the hair as you trim. Also available, a version for professional pet grooming. Great for dogs, cats, horses and any long-haired pet, it will remove burrs, matting, tangles and embedded insects gently, quietly and quickly, and the adjustable blade will trim any type of hair to the desired length. Both are solidly constructed in stainless steel and come with two trimming blades.

Trim & Cut for Hair £9.95 DA27674
Trim & Cut for Pets £9.95 DA27942
Extra Blades (3) £2.50 DB27980

Nick Biggs worked for ten years as a copywriter and creative director for London advertising agencies, and began working freelance in 1990. His very first client was Innovations. Since then he's written just about every word of every Innovations Catalogue: he calculates that he's written copy for more than 5,000 products.

He says, 'In its heyday, the sheer number of catalogues printed was staggering – scary multiples of millions a year. You could always tell when the catalogues had been inserted in the Sunday papers because the floor of WHSmith would be awash with them. But that didn't matter. For all those people who weren't interested in Innovations, there were lots who were. And only a small percentage of readers actually had to buy something to make it a worthwhile business.

'For me, writing Innovations was a labour of love. Technology fascinates me and I love sharing my enthusiasm – especially when talking about gadgets that may just be a bit tongue-in-cheek such as my personal all-time favourites, the sublime NiteMate™ lighted slippers.'

Nick Biggs is forty-nine years old, and is married with two sons. He lives in Cornwall.

INNOVATIONS REPORT

WELCOME TO THE WORLD OF INNOVATIONS. HERE'S HOW TO PLACE YOUR ORDER

BY PHONE (24 HR)
0793 514666

ısing your Credit Card, call during office
speak to one of our friendly customer
istants. We suggest you fill out your order
and then read it to us over the phone.
f office hours our telephone answering
will record details of your order. Please
no. **RX12**

er Services Information Line
13946

e any sort of query about your order, don't
call our Customer Services team. A
f the team will speak to you in person,
u with matters such as despatch dates or
orders. Also call the team if you want
ecific information on any product featured
alogue.

NTEE

satisfaction is guaranteed with Innovations.
ou to be pleased with your order. If for any
roduct from this catalogue fails to give
satisfaction, just return it to us within 14
ceipt for a prompt and courteous refund or
do ask that products be returned in an
ndition, in original packaging and complete
cumentation. This guarantee is in addition
tutory rights.
customers please note that the 14 day test
es not apply to store purchases.

licy on Postage & Packing

s' £2.95 postage and packing charge is the same
x years ago. Remember that you can order any
items you like, and still pay the same postage
g. However, to cover the costs associated with

BY POST: INNOVATIONS REPORT, EUROWAY BUSINESS PARK, SWINDON SN5 8SN

Complete the order form opposite in clear, bold, block capitals, then send the order form to us together with your cheque, postal order, or credit card details.

BY FAX (24 HR)
0793 485636

If you are paying by credit card, you may place your order by fax. Please make sure you write clearly and bol in block capitals and do please remember to give u your day-time telephone number in case of any transmission difficulties. As with all orders, fax orders are acknowledged by post.

DELIVERY

The vast majority of our products are delivered wit 10 days, but please allow up to 28 days to cover any eventuality (particularly in the case of personalised larger items). We can deliver to anywhere in the UK except the Channel Islands.

Auto Light – yours for just £1